Our 50 States Atlas Workbook

Mary Evelyn Notgrass McCurdy, Editor
Donna Ellenburg, Contributing Editor

Maps by Nate McCurdy
Illustrations by Anna Higgins

Washington
Oregon
Idaho
Montana
North Dakota
South Dakota
Wyoming
Nebraska
California
Nevada
Utah
Colorado
Kansas
Arizona
New Mexico
Texas
Pacific
Ocean
Mexico

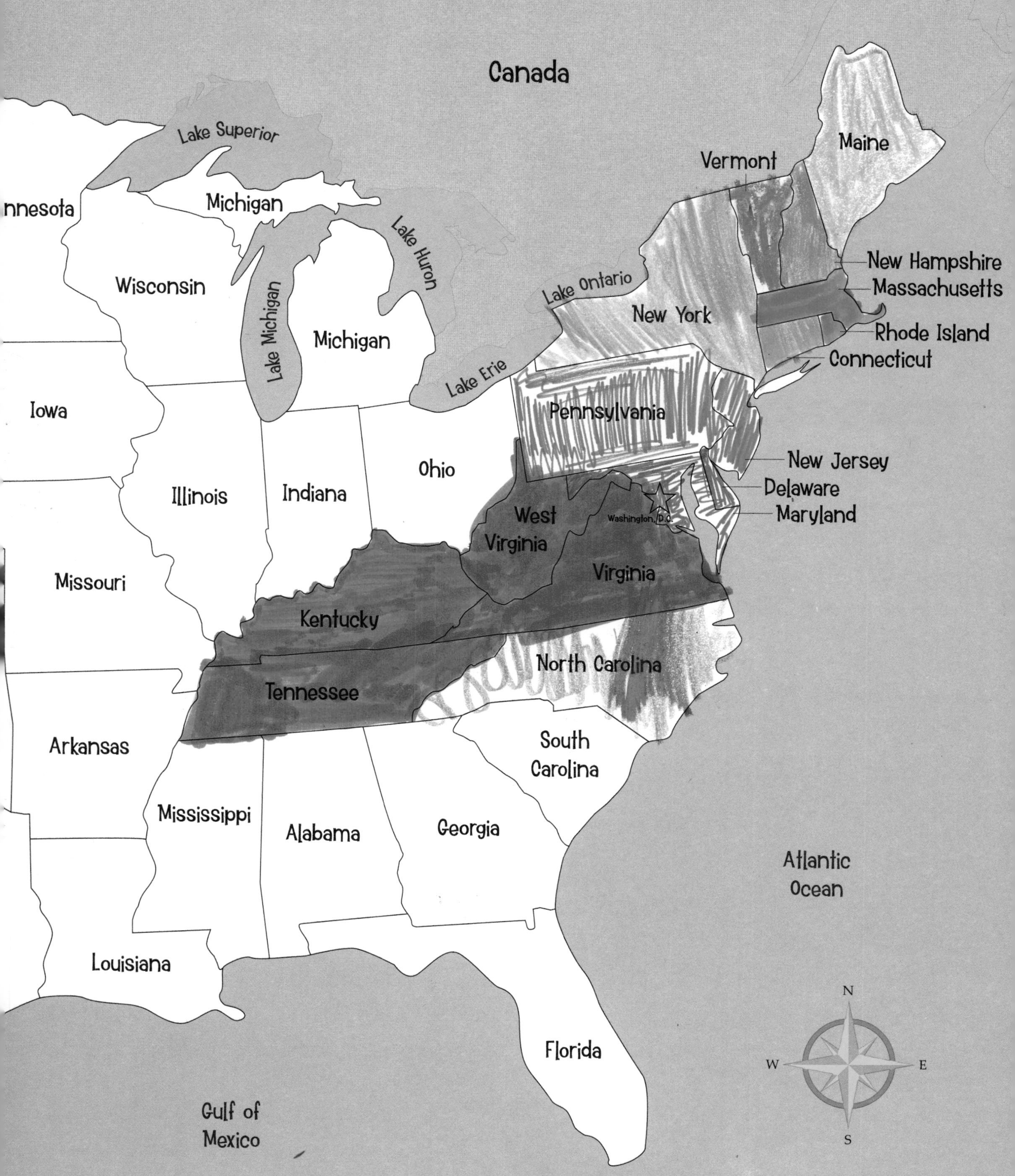
Canada
Lake Superior
nnesota
Michigan
Lake Huron
Wisconsin
Lake Michigan
Michigan
Lake Ontario
Lake Erie
Vermont
Maine
New Hampshire
Massachusetts
New York
Rhode Island
Connecticut
Iowa
Pennsylvania
Ohio
New Jersey
Illinois
Indiana
Delaware
West Virginia
Washington, D.C.
Maryland
Missouri
Virginia
Kentucky
North Carolina
Tennessee
Arkansas
South Carolina
Mississippi
Alabama
Georgia
Atlantic Ocean
Louisiana
N
W
E
Florida
Gulf of Mexico
S

New England: Maine

Write the word **coast** on the blank. A coast can be sandy or rocky. Trace over the faint lines and add your own details to illustrate the rocky coast of Maine. You might like to add a lighthouse or a sailboat.

coast
____

the edge of land near an ocean or sea

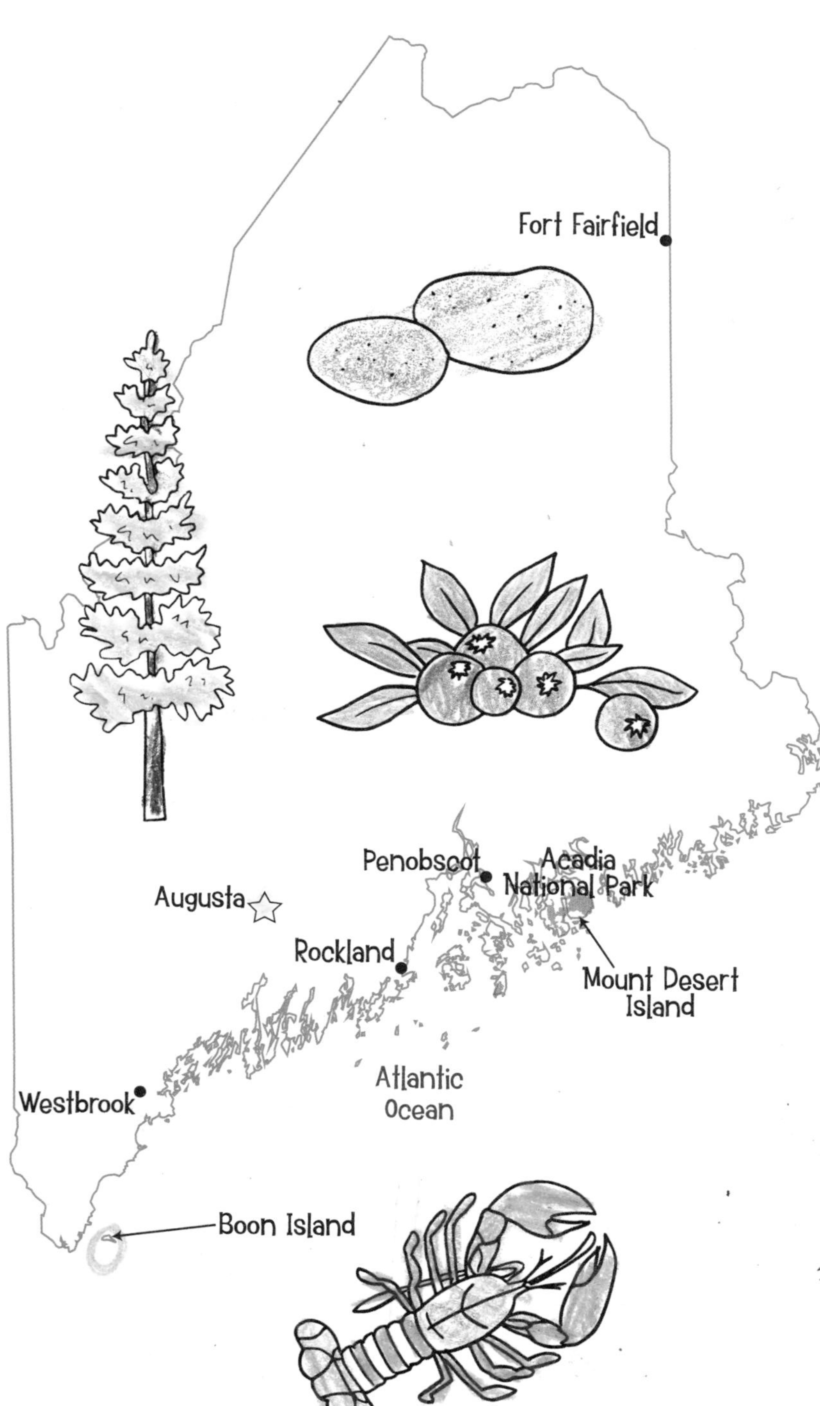

1. Look at the state flag, bird, and tree of Maine pictured on this page. (The white pine cone and tassel is the state flower of Maine.)
2. Color Maine orange on the map on pages 2-3.
3. Color the star that marks Augusta, the capital of Maine, yellow.
4. Draw waves in the Atlantic Ocean.
5. Almost half of Maine's potatoes become french fries. Color the potatoes brown.
6. Trees cover most of Maine. Color the tree.
7. Wild blueberries grow throughout Maine. Color the blueberries.
8. Color the lobster Mary caught in her trap on Boon Island red.

Black-capped chickadee

White pine

New England: New Hampshire

Write the word **gorge** on the blank. Trace over the faint lines and add your own details to illustrate a New Hampshire gorge.

gorge

a narrow valley that usually has steep rocky walls and a stream running through it

1. Look at the state flag, bird, tree, and flower of New Hampshire pictured on this page.
2. Color New Hampshire orange on the map on pages 2-3.
3. Color the star that marks Concord, the capital of New Hampshire, yellow.
4. Draw mountains in the area labeled White Mountains.
5. Color the beryl turquoise.
6. On the amethyst, color the area marked "A" gray. Leave the area marked "B" white. Color the pointed gems on top purple.
7. Color the garnets (the small stones within the larger rock) deep red. Color the rock around the garnets light brown.
8. Draw a tent beside Mount Washington and see if your design can stand up to the wind!

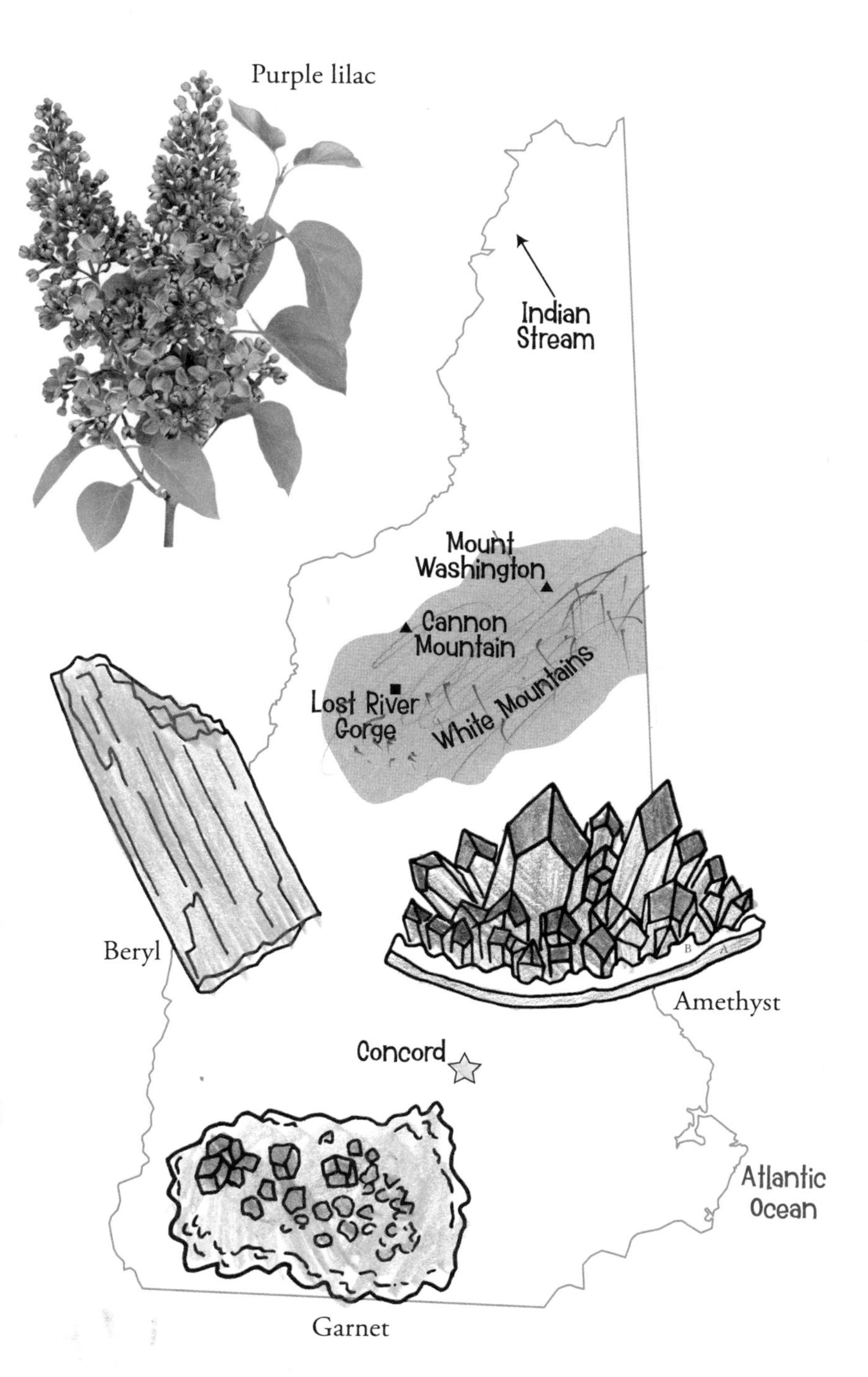

White birch

Purple finch

New England: Vermont

Write the word **quarry** on the blank. Trace over the faint lines and add your own details to illustrate a granite quarry in Vermont.

quarry

a large pit from which stone or other materials are removed from the earth

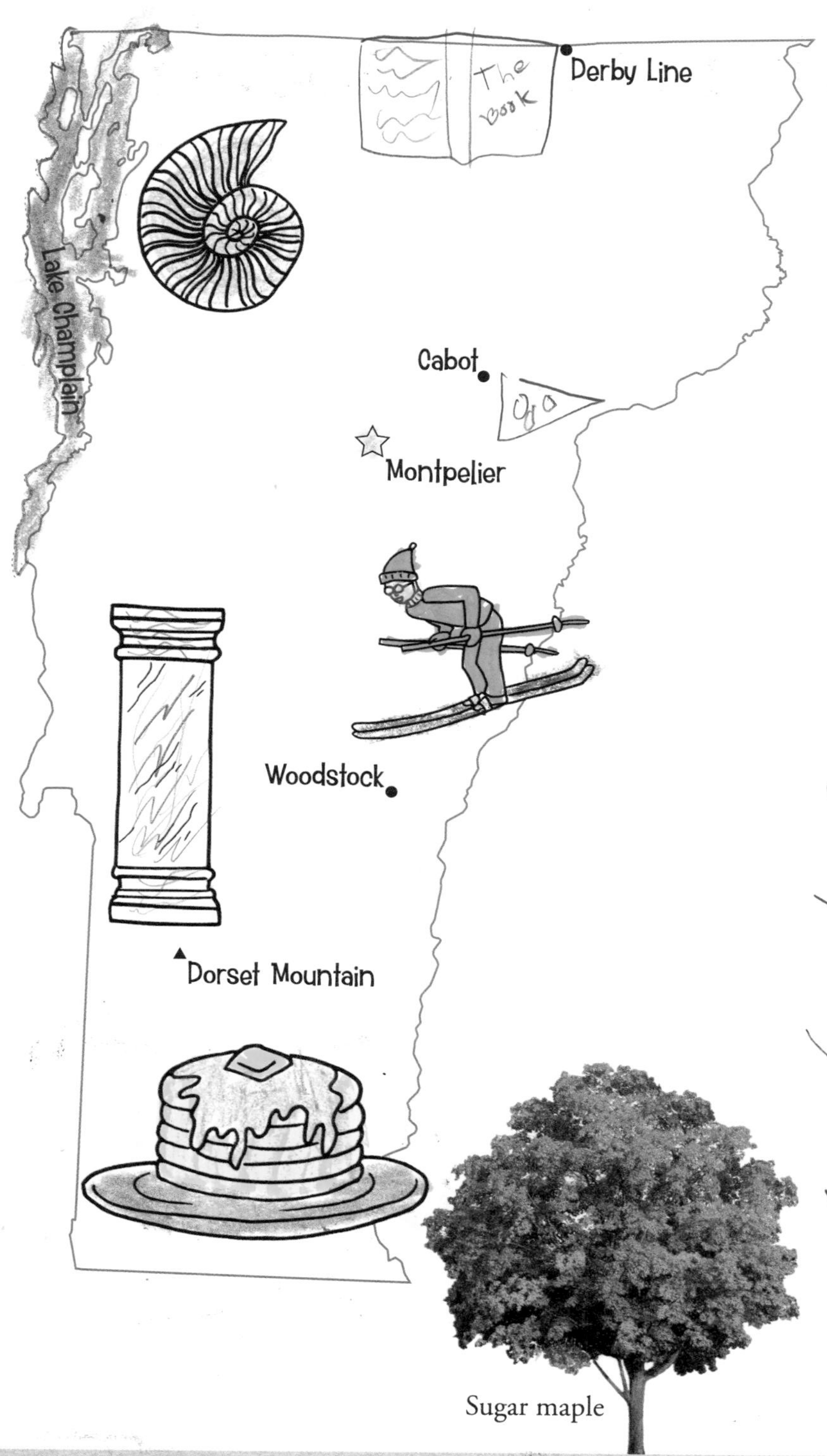

Sugar maple

1. Look at the state flag, bird, tree, and flower of Vermont pictured on this page.
2. Color Vermont orange on the map on pages 2-3.
3. Color the star that marks Montpelier, the capital of Vermont, yellow.
4. Draw a book beside Derby Line to represent the Haskell Free Library on the border between the U.S. and Canada.
5. Color Lake Champlain blue.
6. Color the fossil from Lake Champlain light gray.
7. Draw a block of cheese beside Cabot.
8. Draw more lines on the column to make it look like marble from the Danby Quarry.
9. Color the pancakes that are covered with Vermont maple syrup.
10. Color the skier who is heading down the mountain in Woodstock and will ride the chair lift back to the top.

Hermit thrush

Red clover

New England: Massachusetts

Write the word **cape** on the blank. Trace over the faint lines and add your own details to illustrate Cape Cod. You might want to add a sunrise in the sky or a boat in the water.

cape ______________________

a large piece of land that extends into an ocean or other large body of water

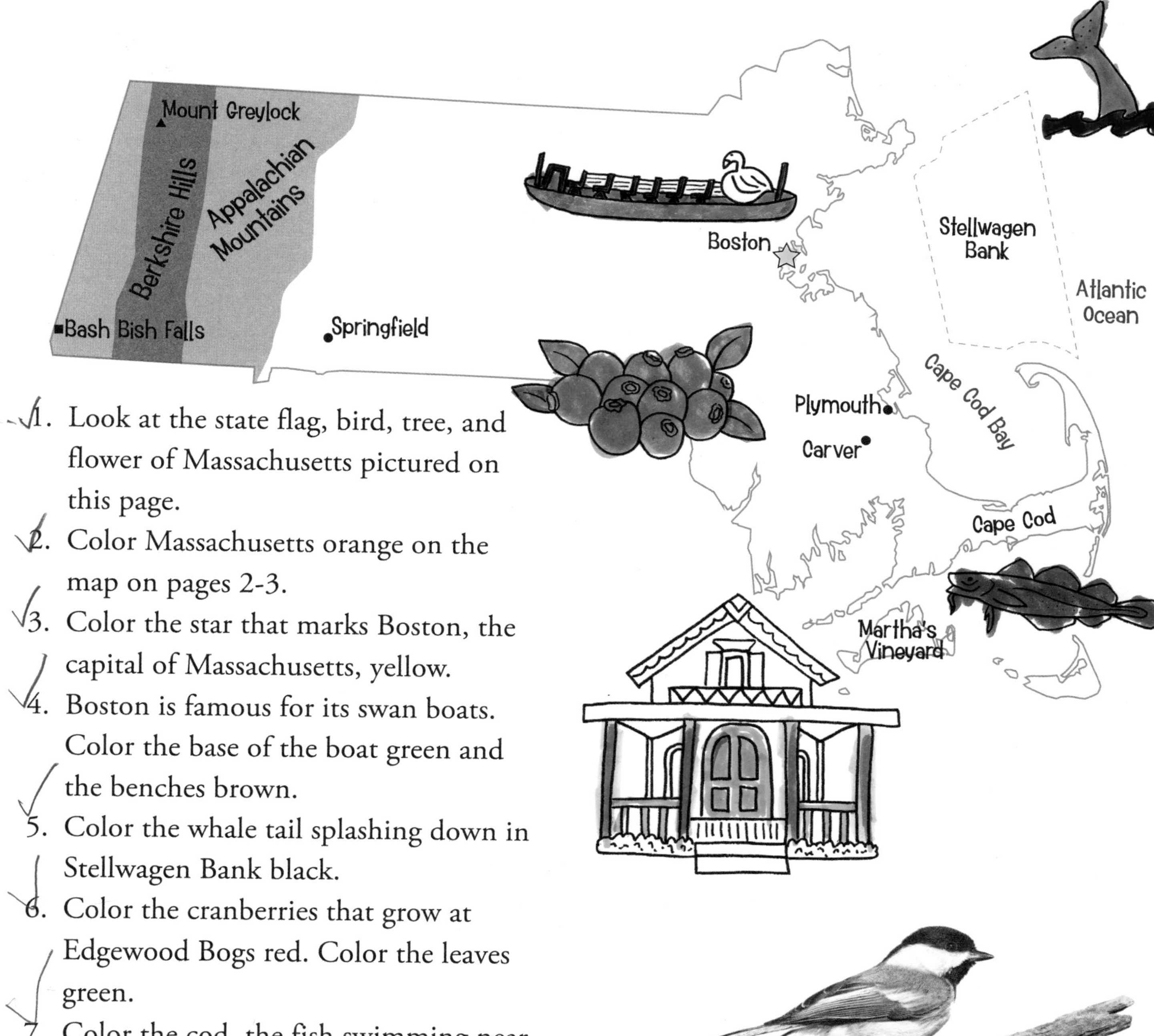

1. Look at the state flag, bird, tree, and flower of Massachusetts pictured on this page.
2. Color Massachusetts orange on the map on pages 2-3.
3. Color the star that marks Boston, the capital of Massachusetts, yellow.
4. Boston is famous for its swan boats. Color the base of the boat green and the benches brown.
5. Color the whale tail splashing down in Stellwagen Bank black.
6. Color the cranberries that grow at Edgewood Bogs red. Color the leaves green.
7. Color the cod, the fish swimming near Cape Cod, brown.
8. Color the Martha's Vineyard cottage with bright colors.

Black-capped chickadee

Mayflower

American elm

New England: Rhode Island

Write the words **salt marsh** on the blank. Trace over the faint lines and add your own details to illustrate a salt marsh in Connecticut. Draw a bird in the nest.

Salt marsh
____

a grassy area that is regularly flooded by water from the ocean

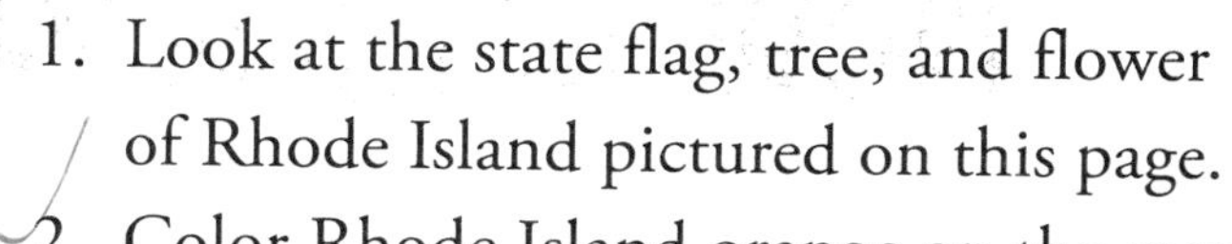

1. Look at the state flag, tree, and flower of Rhode Island pictured on this page.
2. Color Rhode Island orange on the map on pages 2-3.
3. Color the star that marks Providence, the capital of Rhode Island, yellow.
4. Draw waves in the Atlantic Ocean.
5. Color the horse from the Flying Horse Carousel in Watch Hill the colors of your choice.

6. Color The Breakers, the home of Cornelius Vanderbilt in Newport, tan with a red roof.
7. Color the Rhode Island Red, the state bird of Rhode Island, reddish-brown.

Red maple

Violet

New England: Connecticut

Write the word **tide** on the blank. Trace over the faint lines and add your own details to illustrate a tide coming in on the Connecticut coast. Add more posts and the seagull (and maybe a sand castle!).

____

the rising and falling of the sea, which happens twice each day in most coastal areas

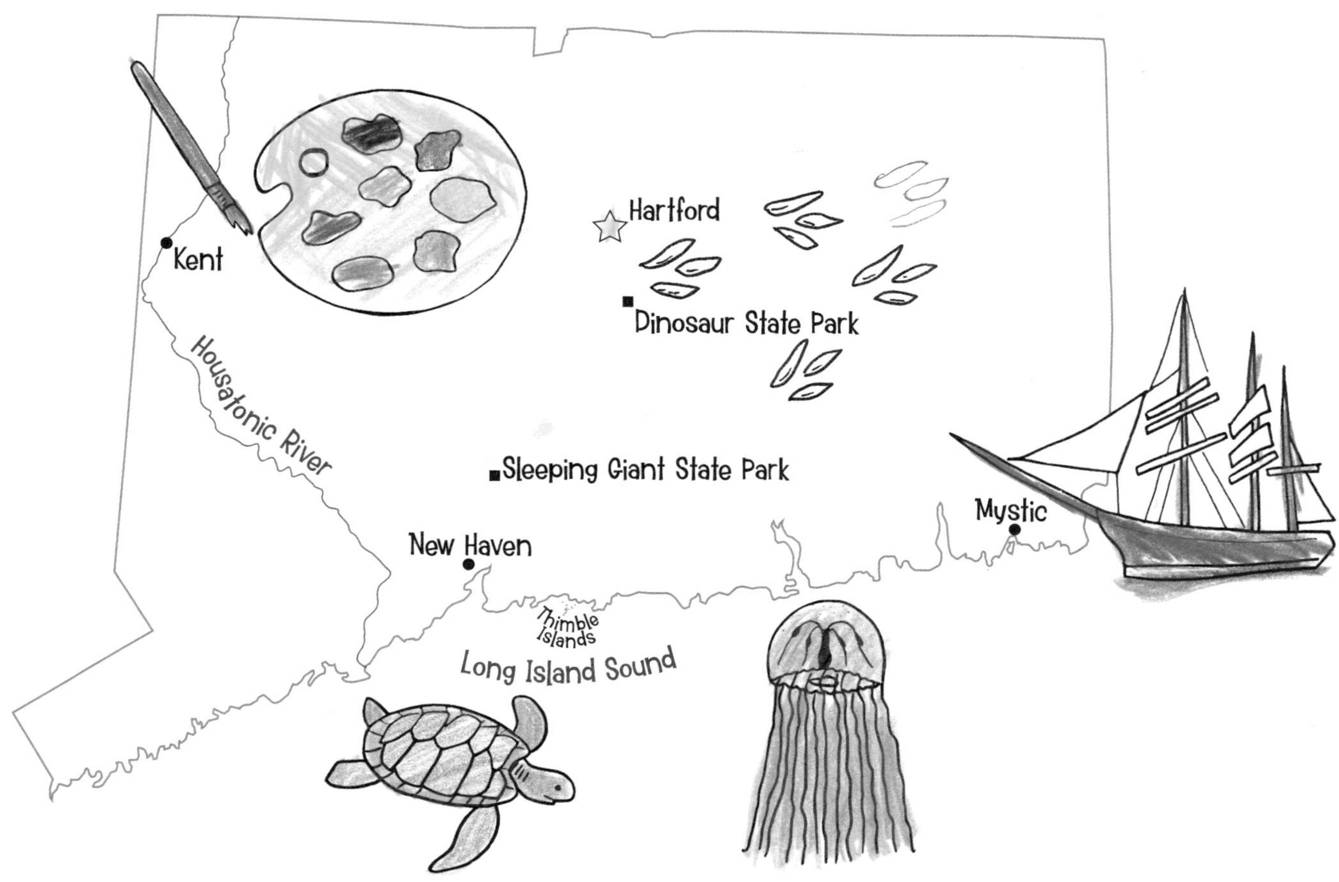

1. Look at the state flag, bird, tree, and flower of Connecticut pictured on this page.
2. Color Connecticut orange on the map on pages 2-3.
3. Color the star that marks Hartford, the capital of Connecticut, yellow.
4. Draw more dinosaur footprints around Dinosaur State Park.
5. Color the ship at the Mystic Seaport Museum. Color the stripe on the bottom of the ship's hull red (the hull is main wooden part of the ship). Color the rest of the hull black.
6. Color the jellyfish in Long Island Sound pink.
7. Color the sea turtle in Long Island Sound green.
8. Color George Nelson's paintbrush. Color the little squirts of paint on his pallet different colors.

Robin

Mountain laurel

Charter oak

Mid-Atlantic: New York

Write the words **river valley** on the blank. Trace over the faint lines and add your own details to illustrate the Hudson River Valley in New York.

river valley

a valley through which a river runs

1. Look at the state flag, bird, tree, and flower of New York pictured on this page.
2. Color New York pink on the map on pages 2-3.
3. Color the star that marks Albany, the capital of New York, yellow.

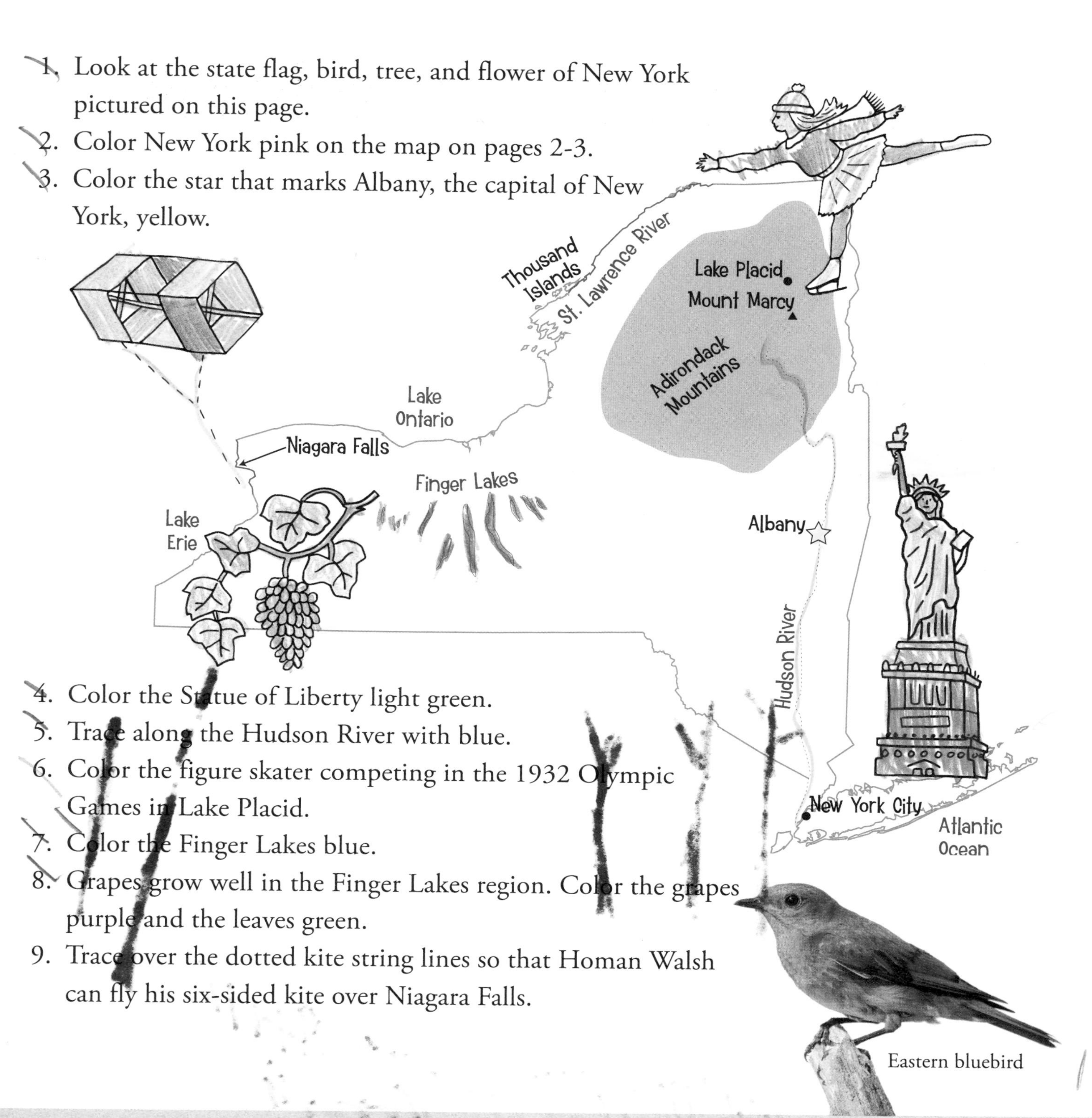

4. Color the Statue of Liberty light green.
5. Trace along the Hudson River with blue.
6. Color the figure skater competing in the 1932 Olympic Games in Lake Placid.
7. Color the Finger Lakes blue.
8. Grapes grow well in the Finger Lakes region. Color the grapes purple and the leaves green.
9. Trace over the dotted kite string lines so that Homan Walsh can fly his six-sided kite over Niagara Falls.

Eastern bluebird

Sugar maple

Rose

Mid-Atlantic: Pennsylvania

Write the word **glen** on the blank. Trace over the faint lines and add your own details to illustrate this scene from Rickets Glen State Park.

glen
____

a narrow valley

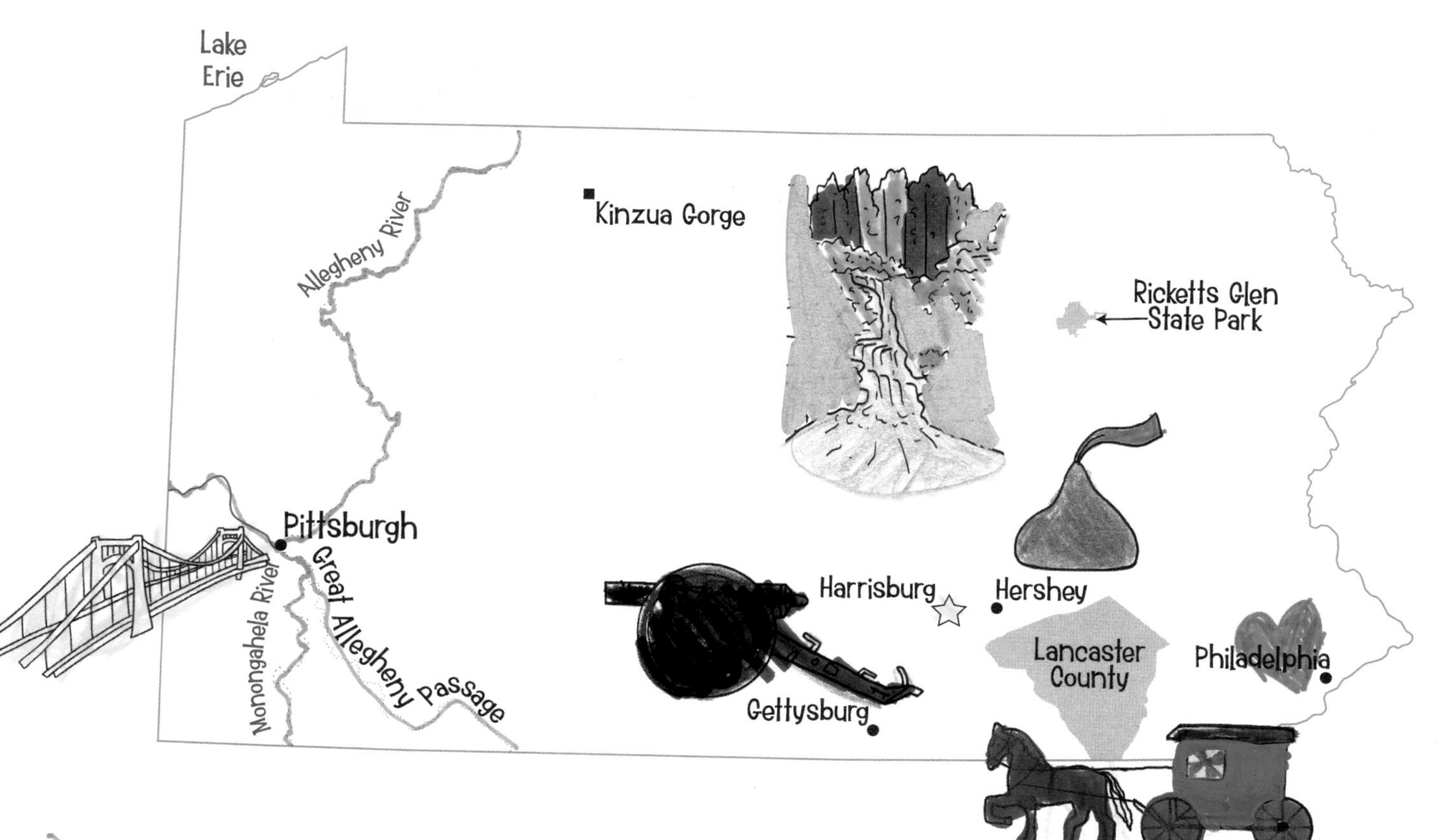

1. Look at the state flag, bird, tree, and flower of Pennsylvania pictured on this page.
2. Color Pennsylvania pink on the map on pages 2-3.
3. Color the star that marks Harrisburg, the capital of Pennsylvania, yellow.
4. Trace along the Monongahela River and the Allegheny River with blue.
5. Color the bridge over Pittsburgh, the City of Bridges, yellow.
6. Use brown and black to color the Civil War cannon beside Gettysburg.
7. Color the wrapped Hershey's Kiss candy beside Hershey silver.
8. Color the Amish buggy black. Color the horse the color of your choice.
9. Draw a heart over Philadelphia, the City of Brotherly Love.
10. Color the waterfall at Ricketts Glen State Park

Mountain laurel

Eastern hemlock

Ruffled grouse

Mid-Atlantic: New Jersey

Write the word **bay** on the blank. Trace over the faint lines and add your own details to illustrate the Delaware Bay.

bay

a body of water partly surrounded by land that connects to a larger body of water

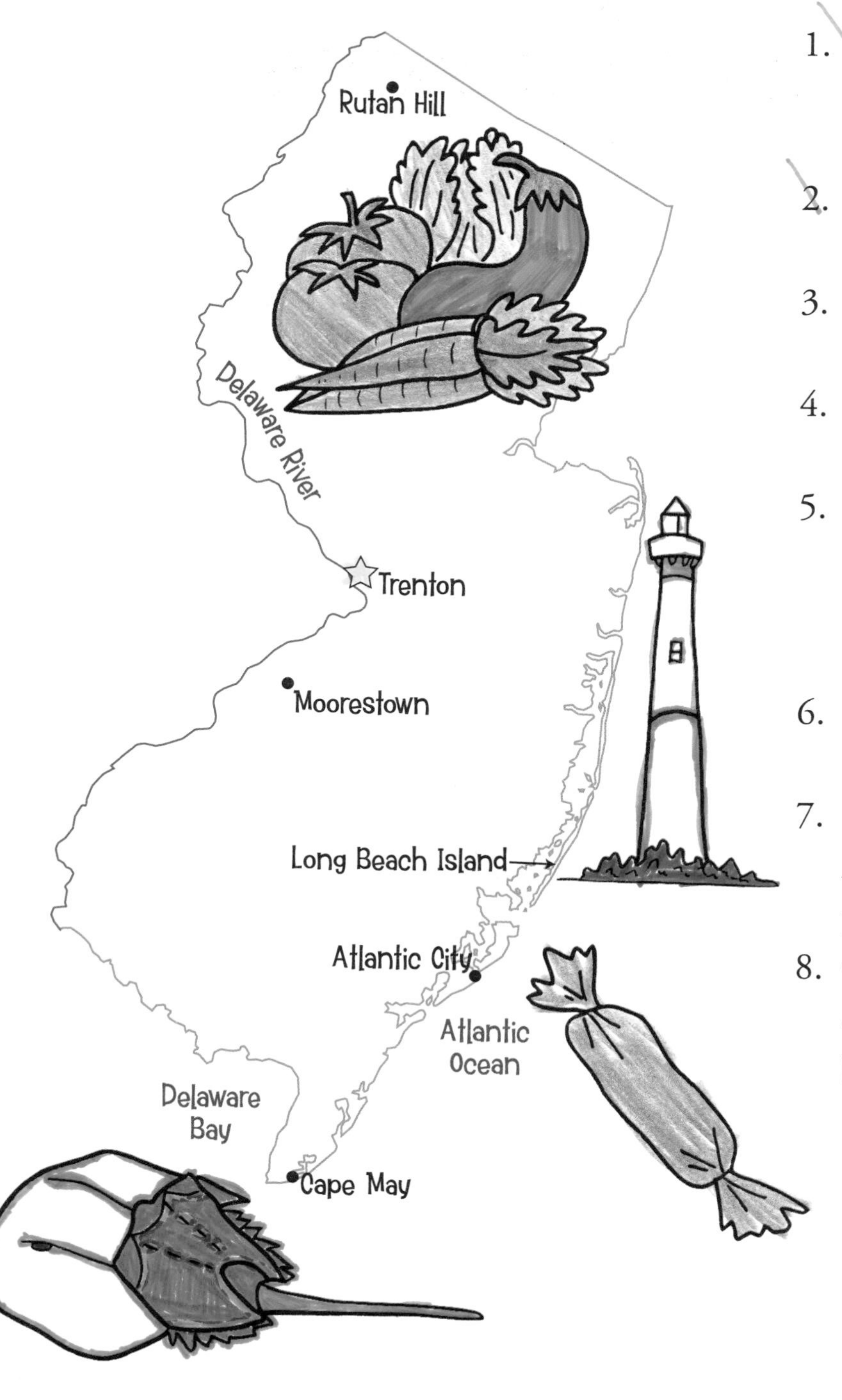

1. Look at the state flag, bird, tree, and flower of New Jersey pictured on this page.
2. Color New Jersey pink on the map on pages 2-3.
3. Color the star that marks Trenton, the capital of New Jersey, yellow.
4. Trace along the Delaware River with blue.
5. New Jersey is the Garden State. Color the carrots orange, the tomatoes red, the eggplant purple, and the lettuce green.
6. Color the top half of Old Barney (the Barnegat Lighthouse) red.
7. Color the saltwater taffy beside Atlantic City the color of the flavor you would like to have.
8. Color the horseshoe crab who has come to lay eggs in Delaware Bay brown.

Violet

Northern red oak

Eastern goldfinch

Mid-Atlantic: Delaware

Write the word **ferry** on the blank. Trace over the faint lines and add your own details to illustrate a ferry crossing Delaware Bay between New Jersey and Delaware.

____

a boat or ship that
regularly carries passengers and goods
across a fairly short distance

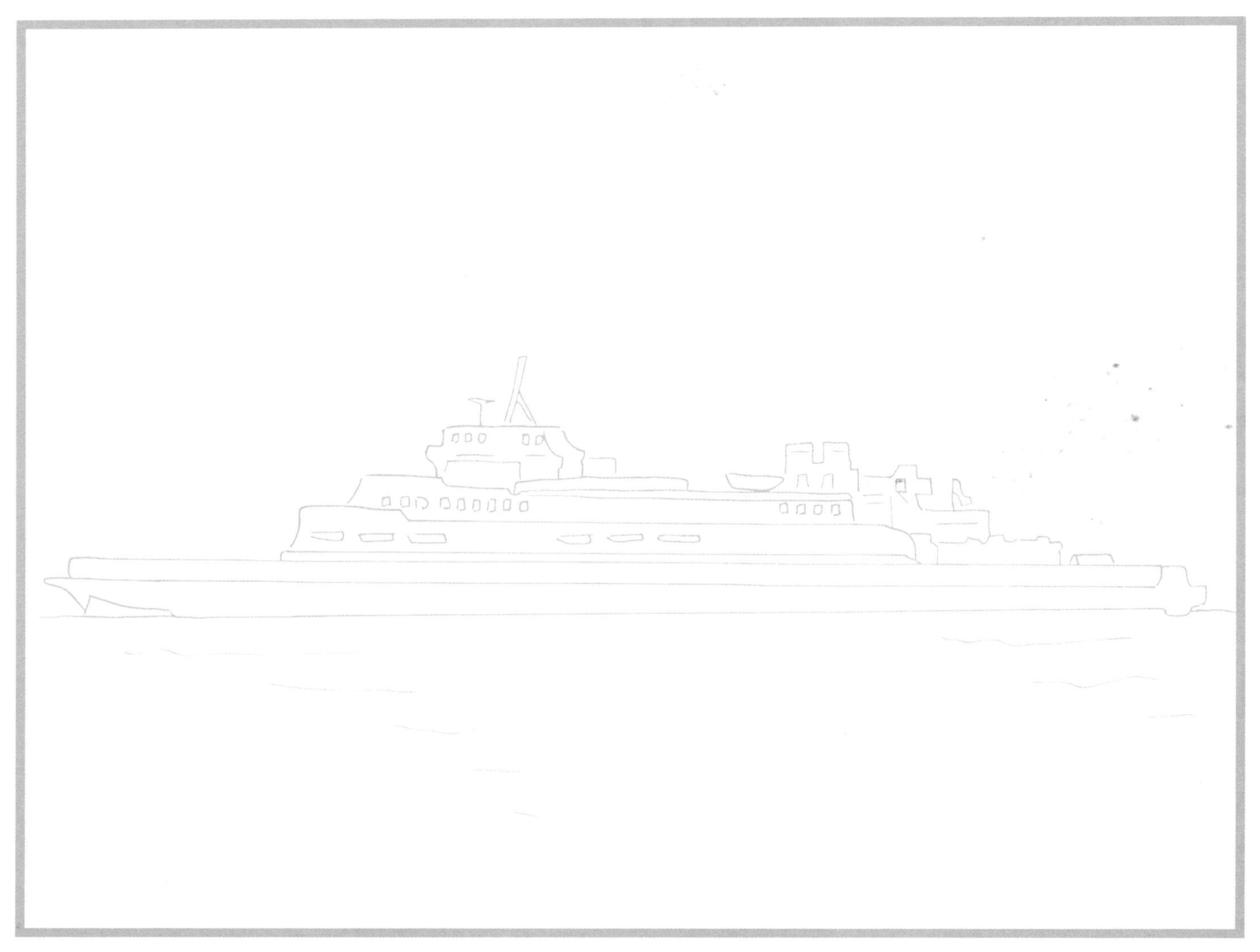

1. Look at the state flag, bird, tree, and flower of Delaware pictured on this page.
2. Color Delaware pink on the map on pages 2-3.
3. Color the star that marks Dover, the capital of Delaware, yellow.
4. Color the menhaden fish in Delaware Bay silver.
5. Color Old State House in Dover red. Color the roof gray.
6. Color the beach umbrella at Rehoboth Beach.
7. Draw waves in the Atlantic Ocean.

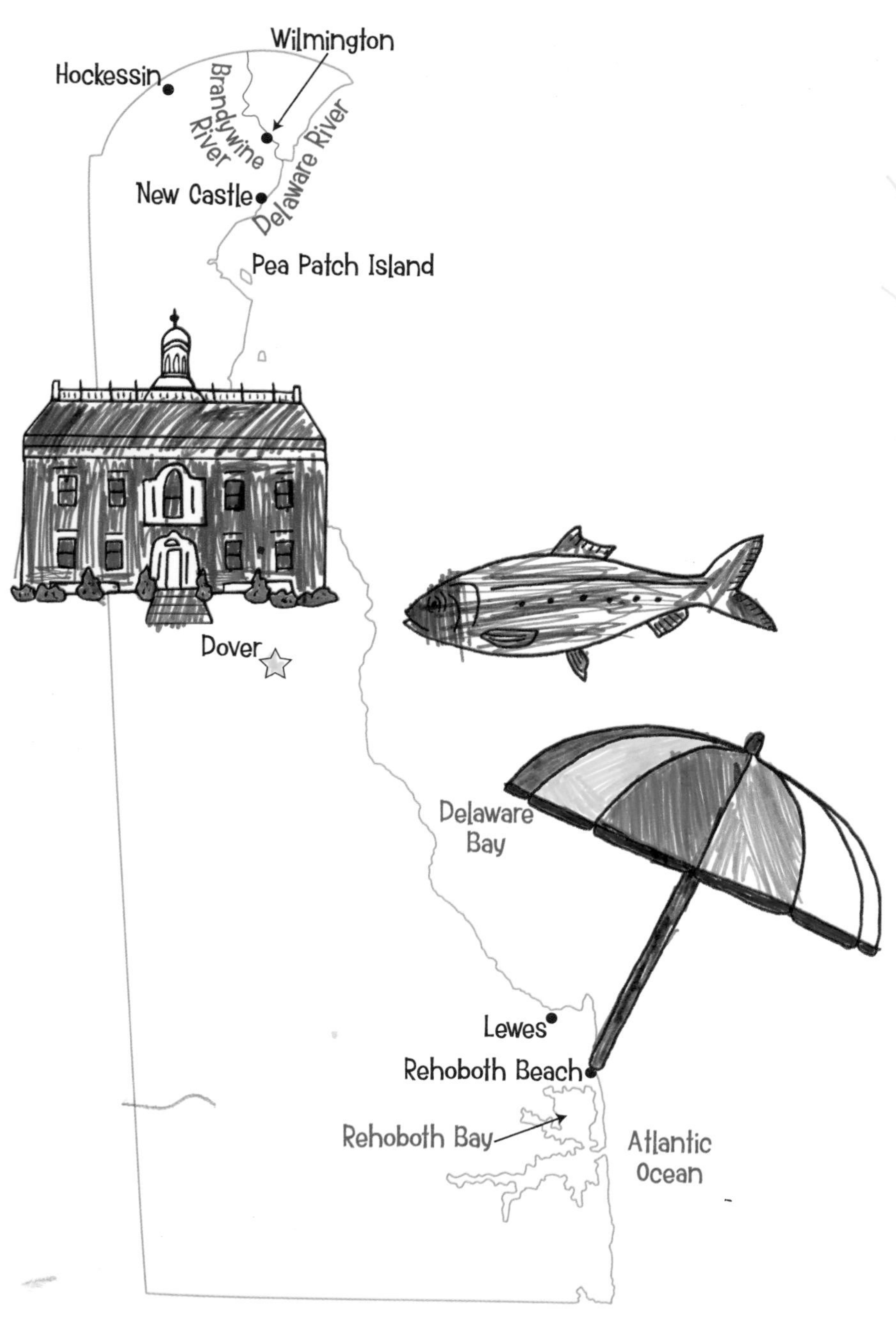

Delaware blue hen

American holly

Peach blossom

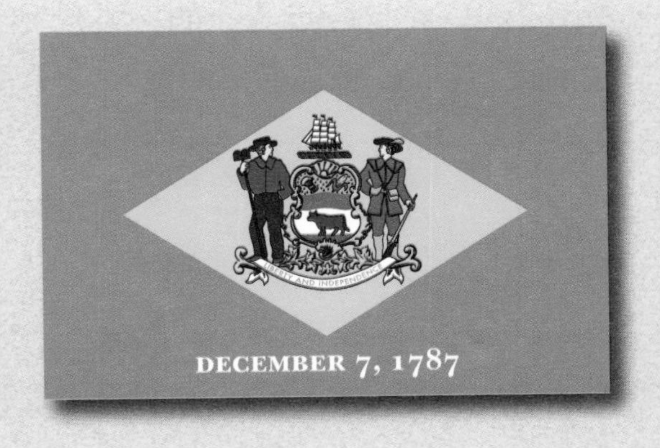

Mid-Atlantic: Maryland

Write the word **estuary** on the blank. Trace over the faint lines and add your own details to illustrate an estuary on the coast of Maryland. Add more tree trunks to the group of distant trees.

estuary
____

an area where rivers and streams meet the ocean

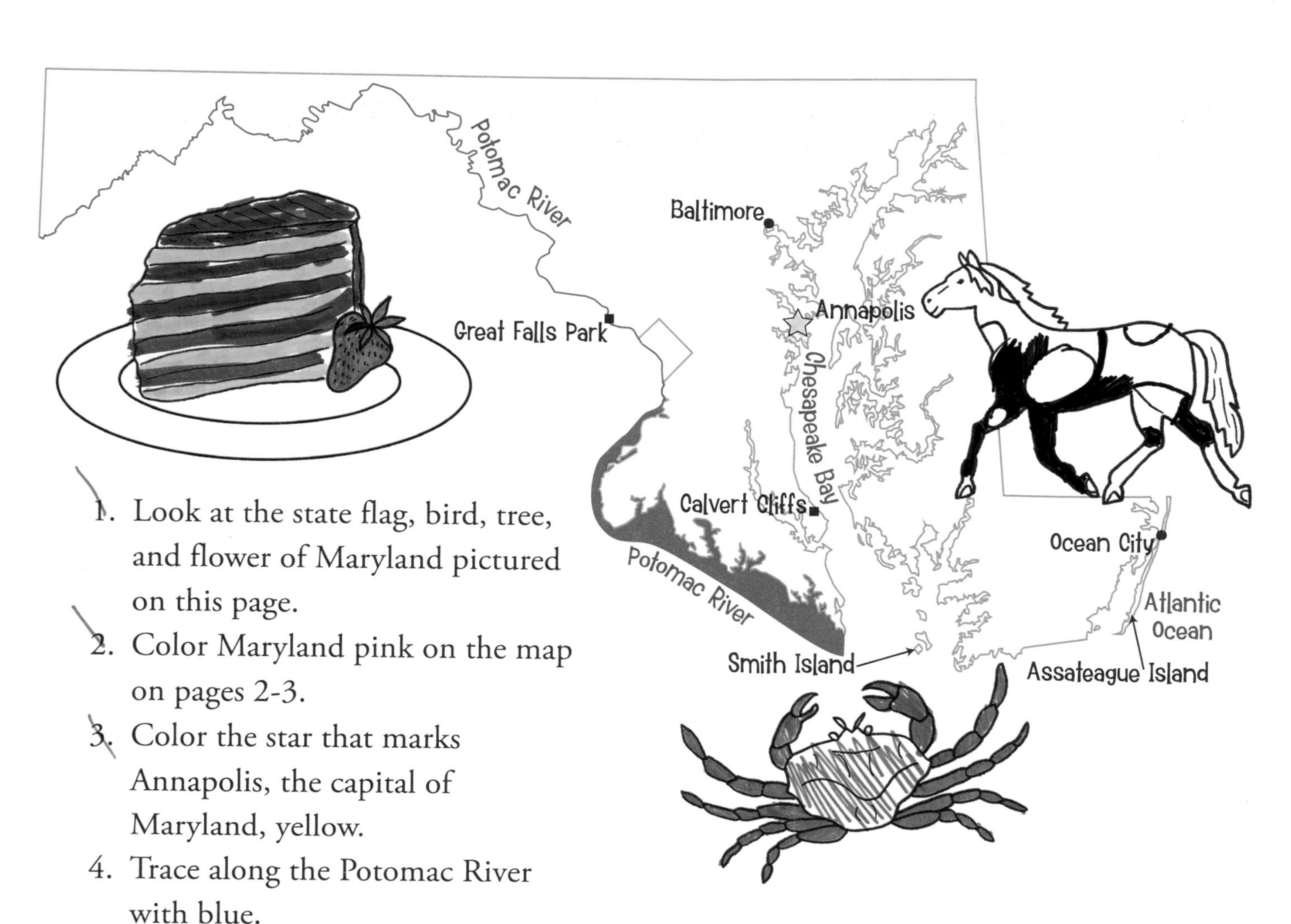

1. Look at the state flag, bird, tree, and flower of Maryland pictured on this page.
2. Color Maryland pink on the map on pages 2-3.
3. Color the star that marks Annapolis, the capital of Maryland, yellow.
4. Trace along the Potomac River with blue.
5. Color the wild horse beside Assateague Island.

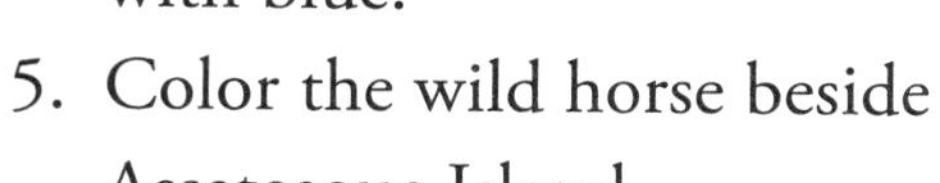

6. Color the crab beside Smith Island red.
7. Color the Smith Island cake, the official dessert of Maryland.

Baltimore oriole

White oak

Black-eyed Susan

Mid-Atlantic: Washington, D.C.

Write the word **memorial** on the blank. Trace over the faint lines and add your own details to illustrate the Lincoln Memorial. Use a ruler to finish drawing the columns. Shade in the three areas between the center columns to show the darkness inside.

____

an object that serves to remind people of a person or event

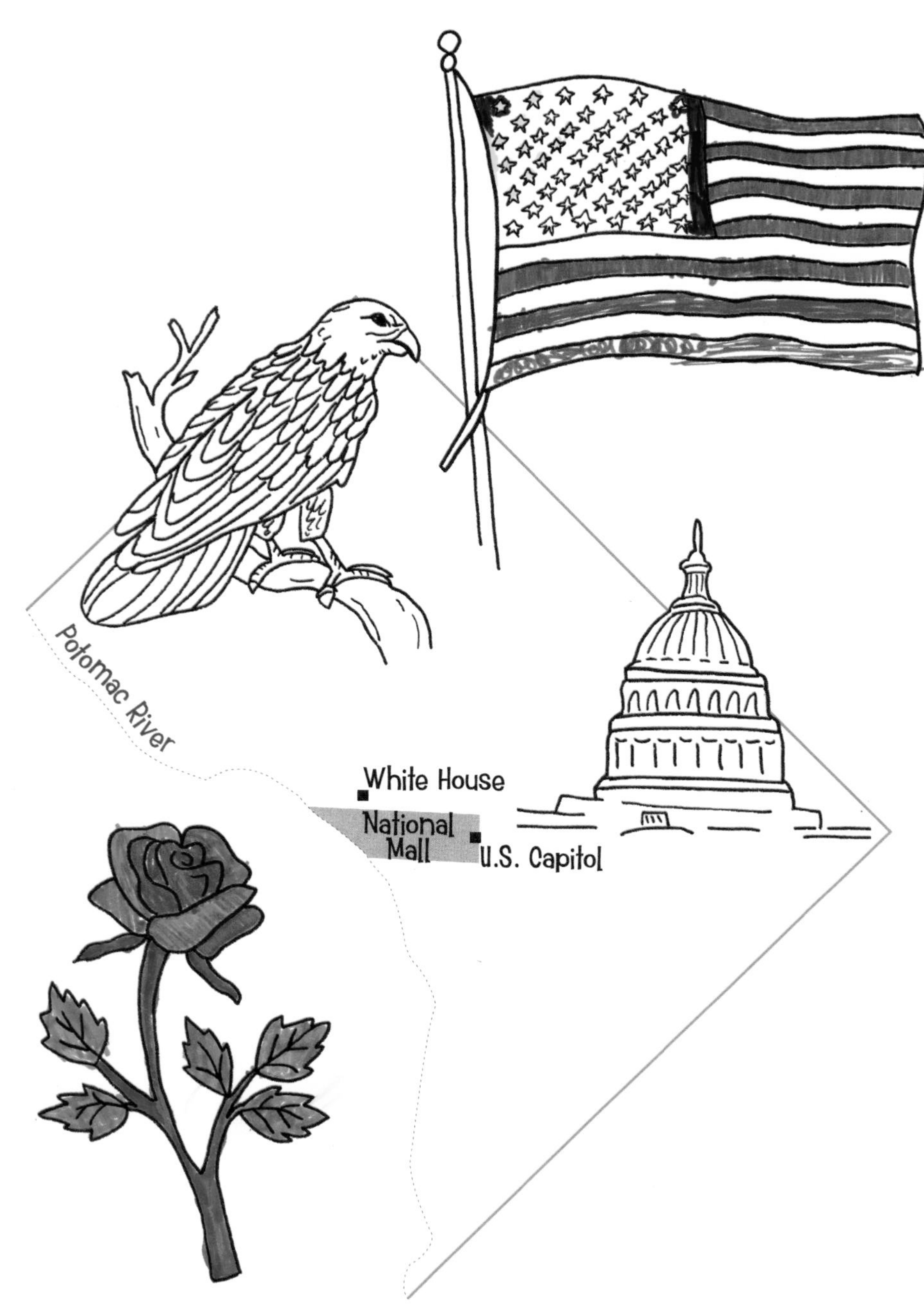

1. Look at the flag, bird, tree, and flower of Washington, D.C., pictured in the blue bar.
2. Color the star that marks Washington, D.C., yellow on the map on pages 2-3.
3. The rose is the national flower of the United States. Color the rose red.
4. Trace along the Potomac River with blue.
5. Color the area behind the stars on the American flag blue. Color the top stripe and every other stripe on the flag red.
6. The bald eagle is the national emblem of the United States. Color the eagle's beak and feet yellow. Leave his head white and color the rest of his feathers brown.

Scarlet oak

Wood thrush

South: Virginia

Write the word **stalactite** on the blank. Trace over the faint lines and add your own details to illustrate a cave in Virginia. You can give your illustration depth by shading the dark areas.

____

an icicle-shaped formation inside a cave
made of calcium salts
deposited by dripping water

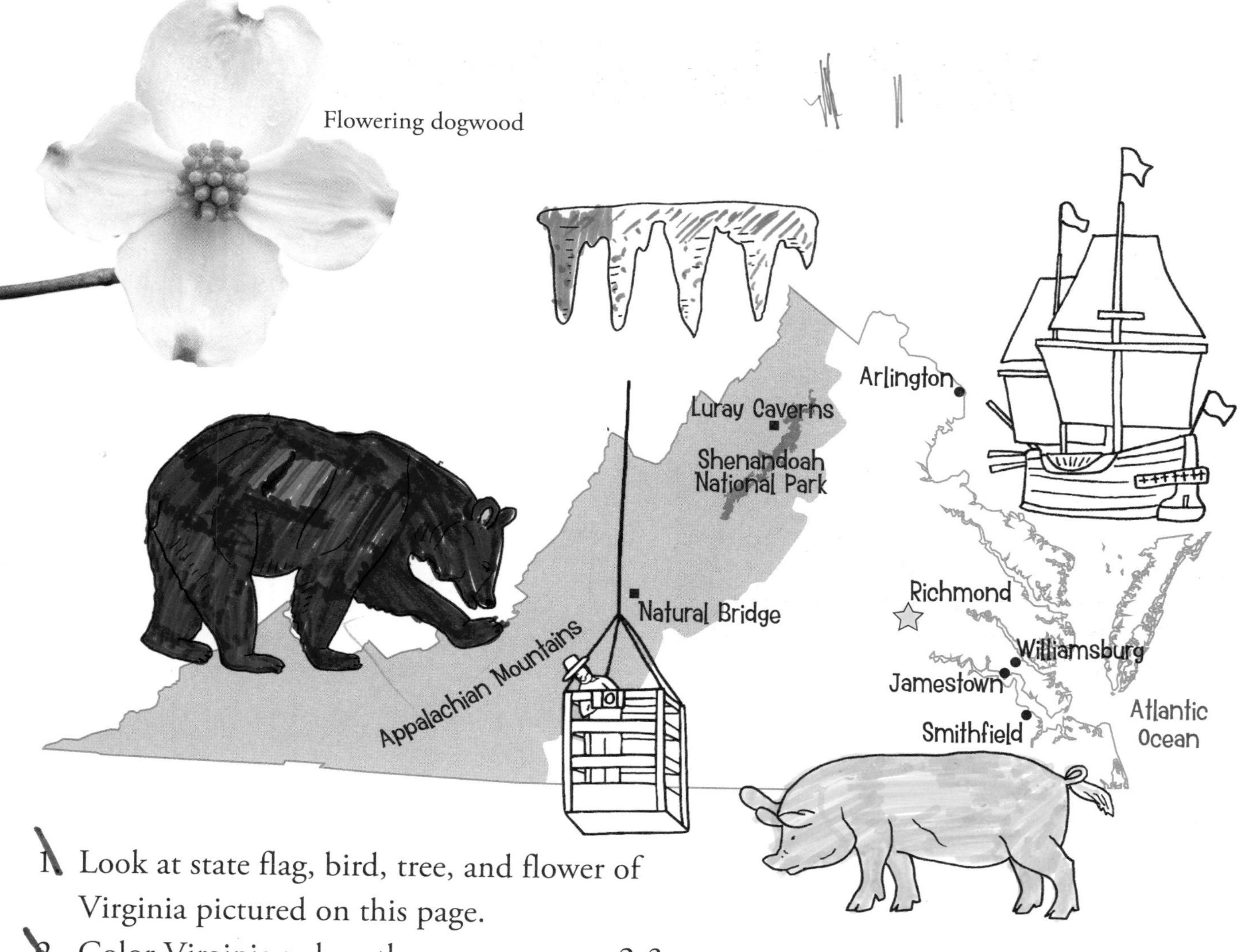

1. Look at state flag, bird, tree, and flower of Virginia pictured on this page.
2. Color Virginia red on the map on pages 2-3.
3. Color the star that marks Richmond, the capital of Virginia, yellow.
4. Color the pig below Smithfield, the Ham Capital of the World, pink.
5. Color the hull of the ship that brought English settlers to Jamestown brown.
6. Draw more stalactites hanging down over Luray Caverns and color them light brown.
7. Draw mountains in the area labeled Appalachian Mountains.
8. Color the bear in the mountains of Virginia black.
9. Color Dr. Reeves in his wooden basket as he photographs the Natural Bridge in 1927.

Flowering dogwood

Northern cardinal

South: West Virginia

Write the word **knob** on the blank. Trace over the faint lines and add your own details to illustrate a knob in West Virginia.

a prominent rounded hill

1. Look at the state flag, bird, tree, and flower of West Virginia pictured on this page.
2. Color West Virginia red on the map on pages 2-3.
3. Color the star that marks Charleston, the capital of West Virginia, yellow.
4. West Virginia is the only state that is completely covered by the Appalachian Mountains. Draw mountains all over the state.
5. Trace the route from Wheeling to Charleston, then back to Wheeling, then back to Charleston. Use blue and trace along the Ohio and Kanawha Rivers to represent the capital moving back and forth between the cities in the 1800s.

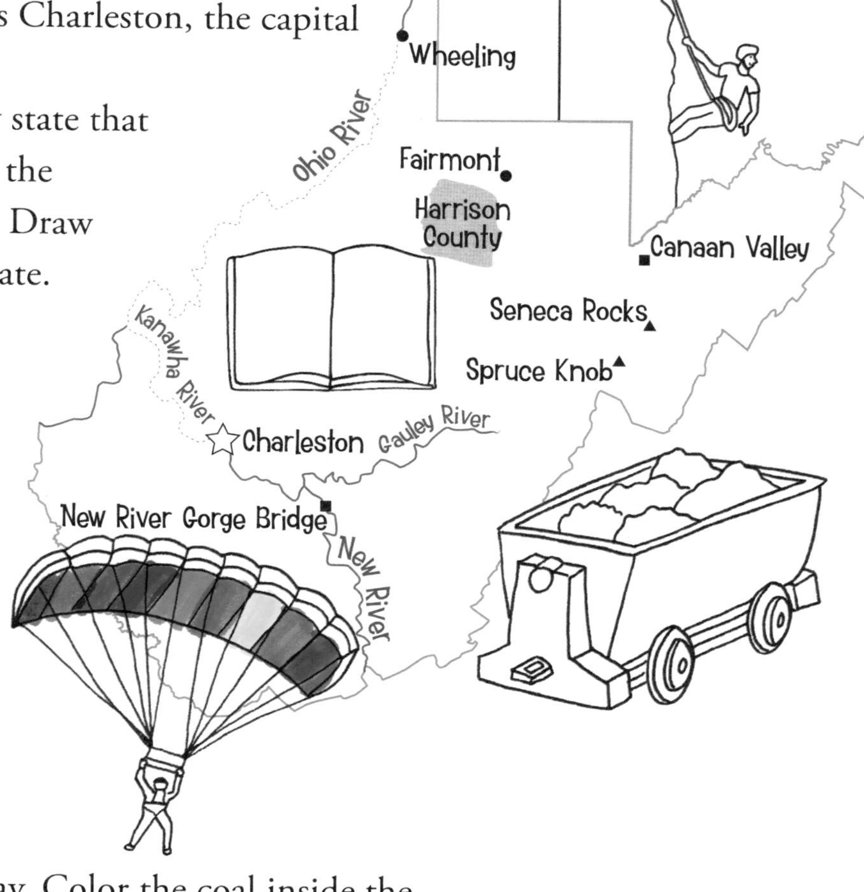

6. Color the mining cart gray. Color the coal inside the mining cart black.
7. Use bright colors to color the parachute under the New River Gorge Bridge.
8. Write some math problems in Luther Haymond's school book.

Northern cardinal

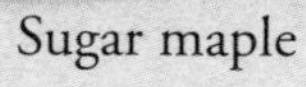
Sugar maple

Rhododendron

South: Kentucky

Write the word **moonbow** on the blank. Trace over the faint lines and add your own details to illustrate a moonbow over Cumberland Falls in Kentucky.

moonbow

a rainbow that appears when the light of the moon shines just right on water droplets in the air

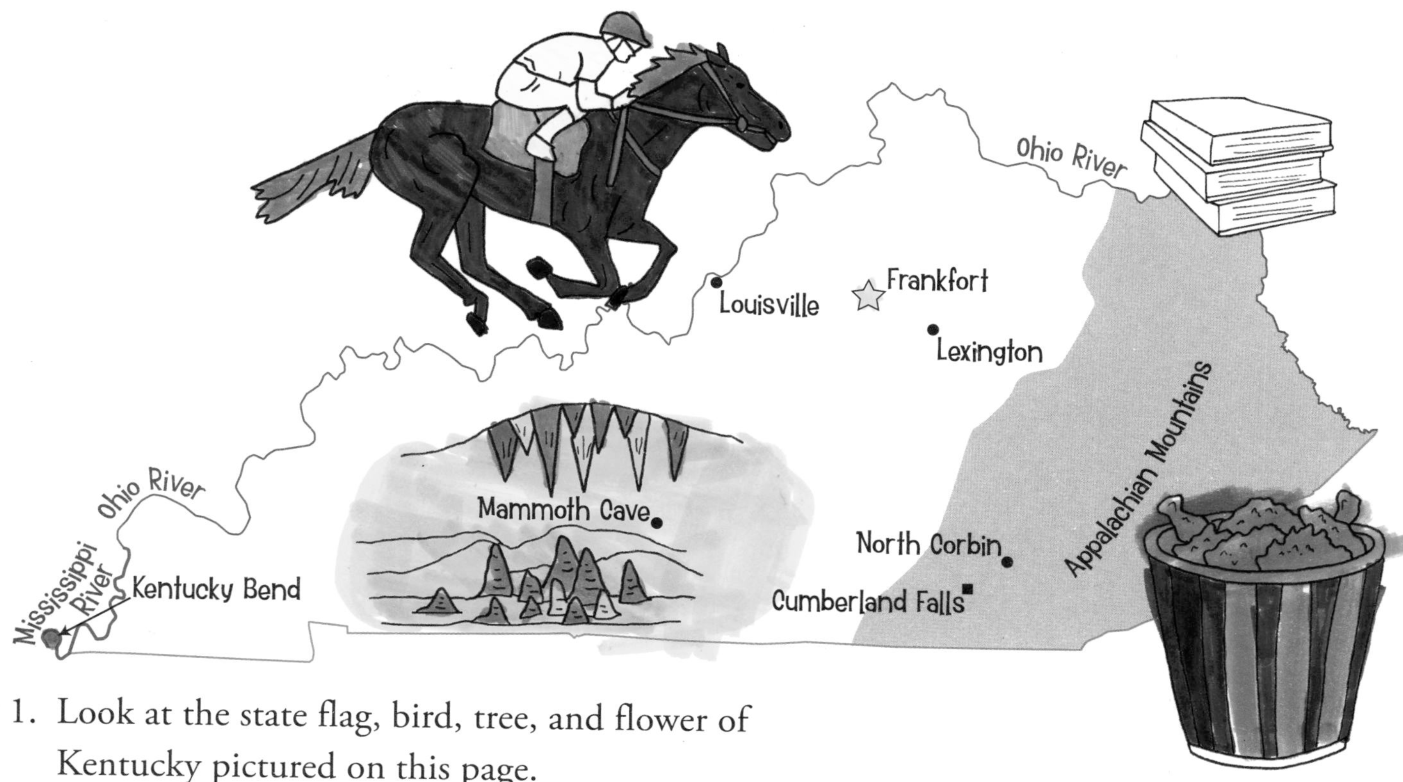

1. Look at the state flag, bird, tree, and flower of Kentucky pictured on this page.
2. Color Kentucky red on the map on pages 2-3.
3. Color the star that marks Frankfort, the capital of Kentucky, yellow.
4. Color the horse and rider racing in the Kentucky Derby in Louisville the colors of your choice.
5. Color the Kentucky Bend green.
6. Color the Mammoth Cave formations brown.
7. Color every other stripe on the bucket red. Color the Kentucky Fried Chicken inside the bucket brown.
8. Draw mountains in the area labeled Appalachian Mountains.
9. Color the books a pack horse librarian carried through the Appalachian Mountains.

Goldenrod

Tulip poplar

Northern cardinal

South: Tennessee

Write the words **underground lake** on the blank. Trace over the faint lines and add your own details to illustrate the Lost Sea in Tennessee.

underground

a lake below the surface of the ground

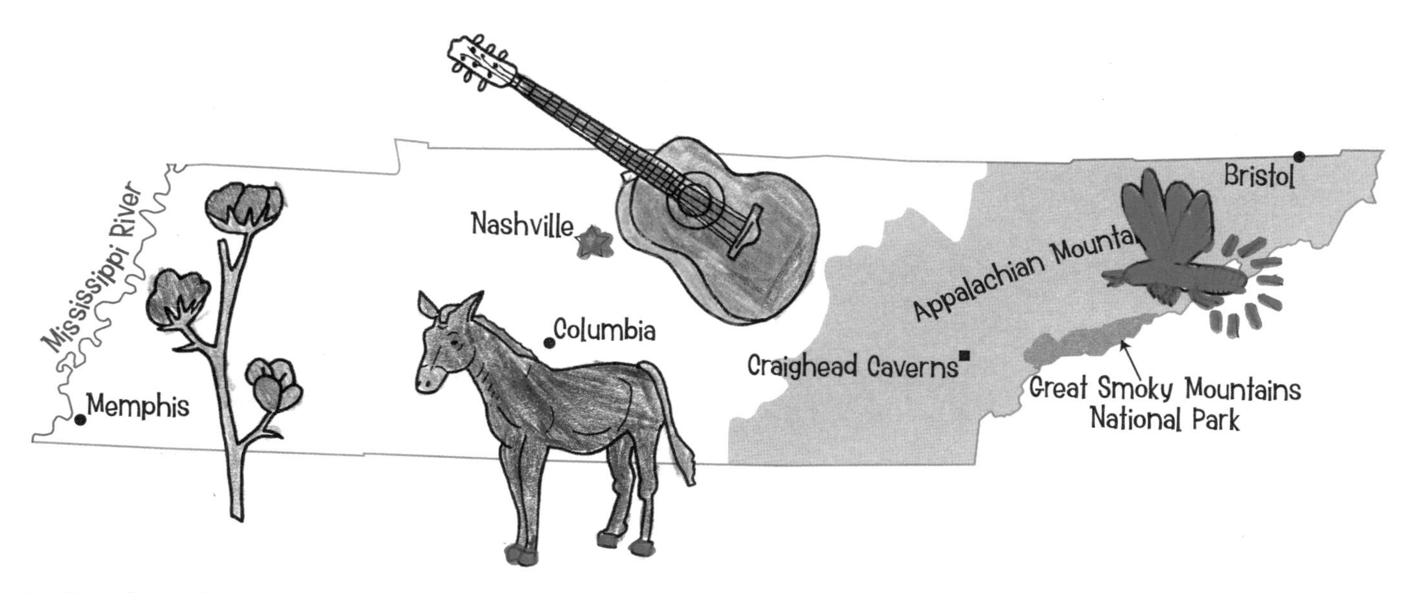

1. Look at the state flag, bird, tree, and cultivated flower of Tennessee pictured on this page.
2. Color Tennessee red on the map on pages 2-3.
3. Color the star that marks Nashville, the capital of Tennessee, yellow.
4. Make the firefly light up by coloring its back section yellow. Color its head red. Color the rest of its body and its top wings black. Color its other set of wings gray.
5. Color the guitar beside Nashville, the Music City, the color of your choice.
6. Color the mule beside Columbia, the Mule Capital of the World, brown or gray.
7. Draw another cotton plant beside Memphis, the city that was once the Cotton Capital of the World.

Tulip poplar

Mockingbird

Iris

South: North Carolina

Write the words **barrier island** on the blank. Trace over the faint lines and add your own details to illustrate a barrier island off the coast of North Carolina.

____

a long, narrow island that protects the mainland from strong winds and damaging ocean waves

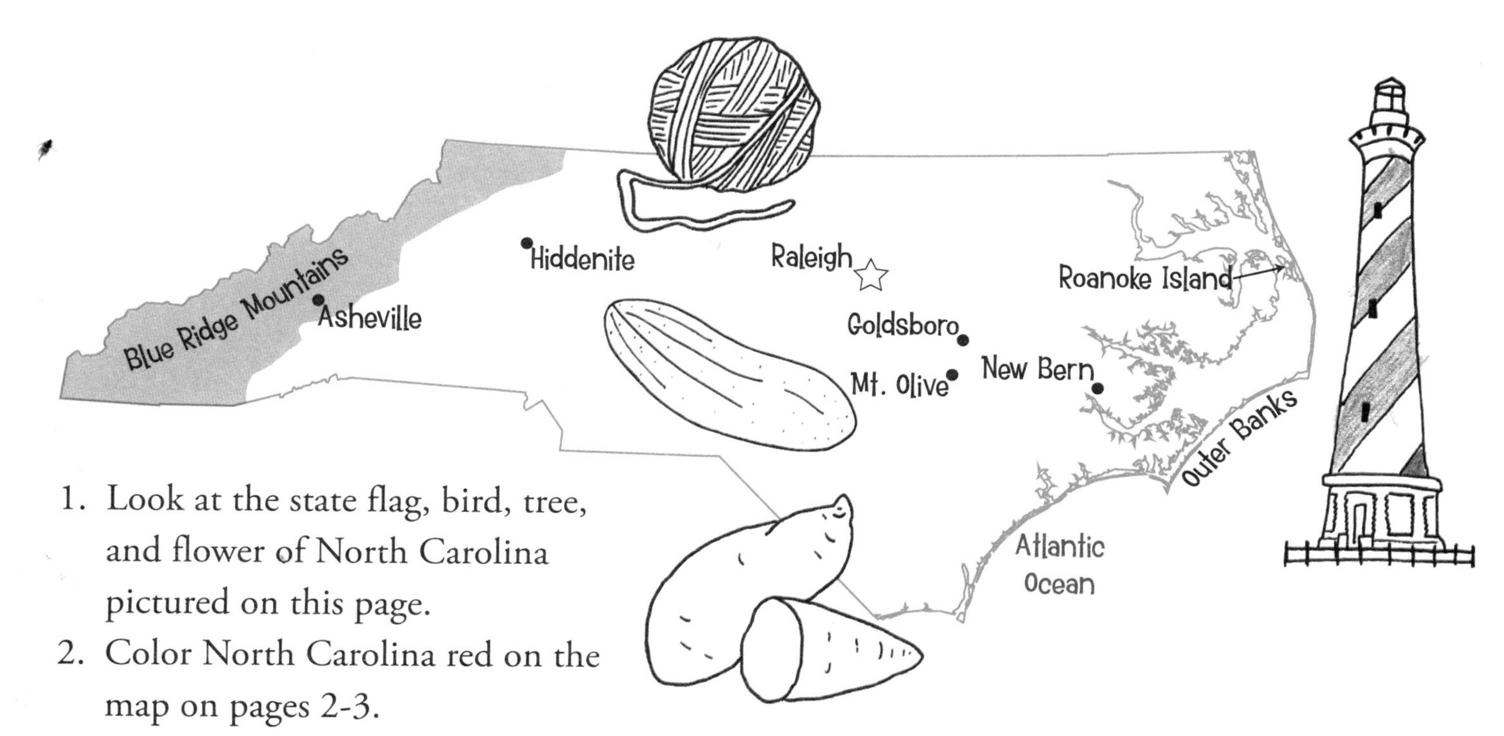

1. Look at the state flag, bird, tree, and flower of North Carolina pictured on this page.
2. Color North Carolina red on the map on pages 2-3.
3. Color the star that marks Raleigh, the capital of North Carolina, yellow.
4. Color the yarn. Draw another ball of yarn beside it to represent North Carolina's textile industry.
5. Draw mountains in the area labeled Blue Ridge Mountains.
6. Color the sweet potatoes brown on the outside and orange on the inside.
7. Color the base of the Cape Hatteras lighthouse red. Color every other stripe black. Draw rays of yellow light coming out of the top.
8. Draw waves along the Outer Banks and in the Atlantic Ocean.
9. Color the cucumber beside Mt. Olive green.

Northern cardinal

Dogwood

Pine

South: South Carolina

Write the words **champion trees** on the blank. Trace over the faint lines and add your own details to illustrate a huge tree in Congaree National Park.

____

a tree that is judged to be
the largest of its species, based on its height,
trunk size, and crown spread

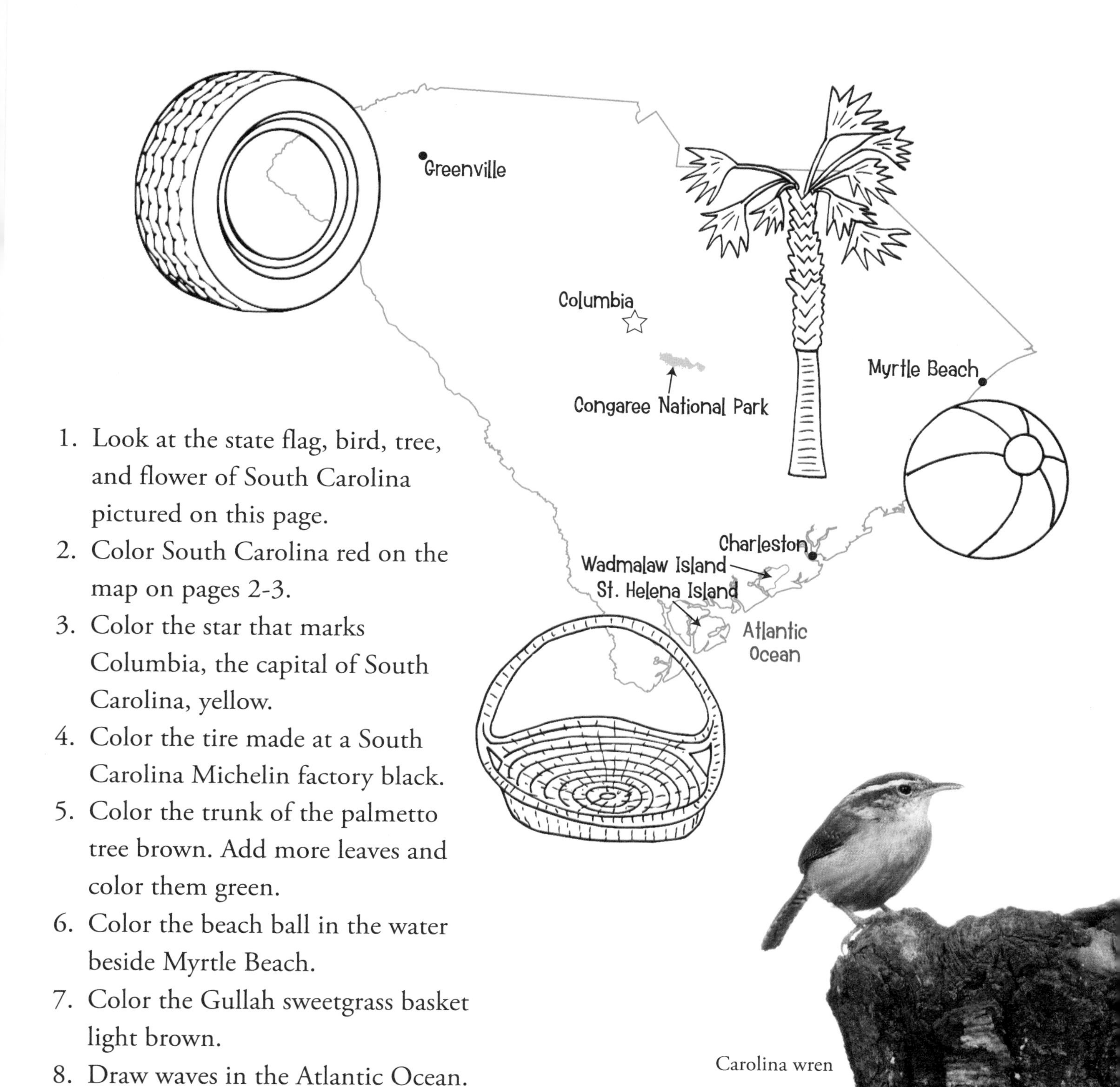

1. Look at the state flag, bird, tree, and flower of South Carolina pictured on this page.
2. Color South Carolina red on the map on pages 2-3.
3. Color the star that marks Columbia, the capital of South Carolina, yellow.
4. Color the tire made at a South Carolina Michelin factory black.
5. Color the trunk of the palmetto tree brown. Add more leaves and color them green.
6. Color the beach ball in the water beside Myrtle Beach.
7. Color the Gullah sweetgrass basket light brown.
8. Draw waves in the Atlantic Ocean.

Carolina wren

Sabal palmetto

Yellow jessamine

South: Georgia

Write the word **swamp** on the blank. Trace over the faint lines and add your own details to illustrate a swamp in Georgia.

____

an area of low ground where water collects

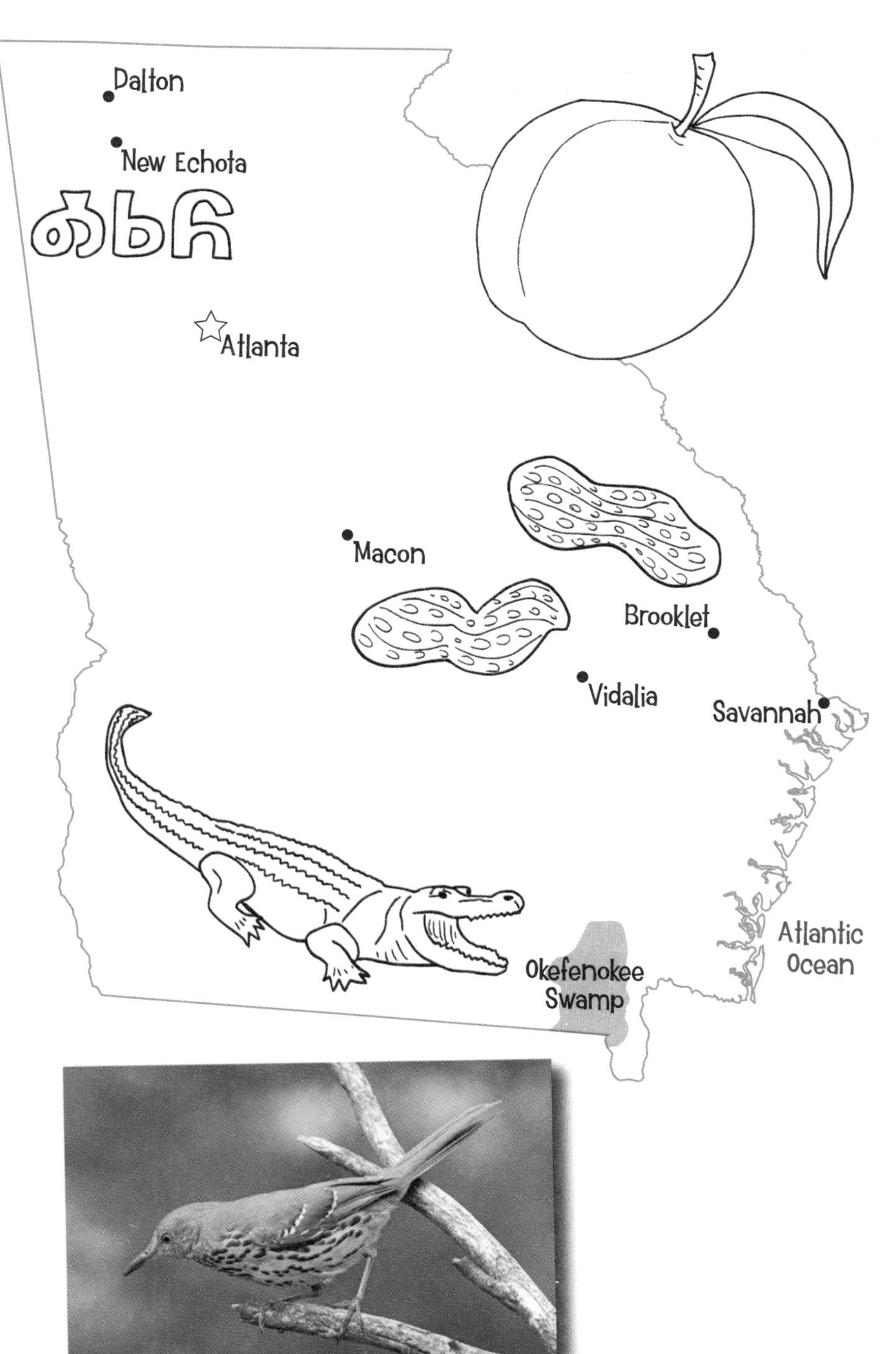

Brown thrasher

1. Look at the state flag, bird, tree, and flower of Georgia pictured on this page.
2. Color Georgia red on the map on pages 2-3.
3. Color the star that marks Atlanta, the capital of Georgia, yellow.
4. Georgia is the Peach State. Color the peach.
5. Trace around the Okefenokee Swamp with green.
6. Color Oscar the Alligator green.
7. Color the Cherokee letters beside New Echota. They spell a Cherokee greeting and are pronounced "O-see-yo."
8. Georgia raises more peanuts than any other state. Color the peanuts brown.

Cherokee rose

Live oak

South: Alabama

Write the word **shoal** on the blank. Trace over the faint lines and add your own details to illustrate the former shoals on the Tennessee River in Alabama.

____

a sandy or rocky area in water that makes the water shallow

1. Look at the state flag, bird, tree, and flower of Alabama pictured on this page.
2. Color Alabama red on the map on pages 2-3.
3. Color the star that marks Montgomery, the capital of Alabama, yellow.
4. Half of all the snails that live in the United States live in Alabama. Color the snail gray and its shell light brown.
5. Draw tiny blue dots around Dismals Canyon to represent the dismalites that shine their bright blue lights there.
6. Trace along the Tennessee River with blue.
7. Use red to write "USA" on the rocket beside Huntsville, the Rocket City.
8. Color the fire hydrant beside Albertville, the Fire Hydrant Capital of the World, red.
9. Draw sand dunes (small rounded hills of sand) along Alabama's coast on the Gulf of Mexico.
10. Color the soldier marching in the Veteran's Day parade in Birmingham.

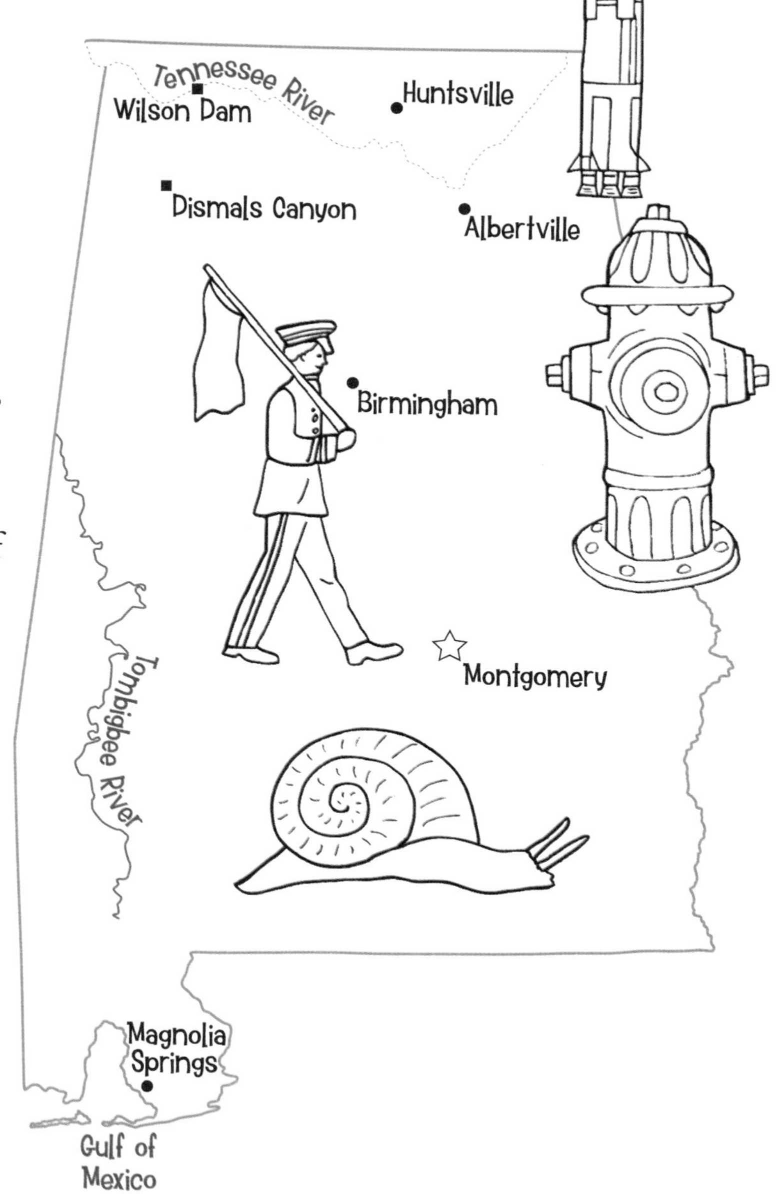

Camellia

Southern longleaf pine

Northern flicker

South: Mississippi

Write the word **delta** on the blank. Trace over the faint lines and add your own details to illustrate the Mississippi River Delta.

____

a wetland that forms where a river empties its water into another body of water

1. Look at the state bird and tree of Mississippi pictured on this page.
2. Color Mississippi red on the map on pages 2-3.
3. Color the star that marks Jackson, the capital of Mississippi, yellow.
4. The magnolia is the state flower of Mississippi. Color the magnolia leaves green. Color the center of the blossom yellow. Leave the petals white.
5. Draw and color an outfit on the catfish statue beside Belzoni, the Catfish Capital of the World.
6. Trace around the Mississippi Delta with green.
7. Color the Natchez mansion the color you would paint it if it were your house.
8. Color the dog who was trained on Cat Island during World War II.
9. Draw beams of light shining out of the top of the Biloxi Lighthouse.

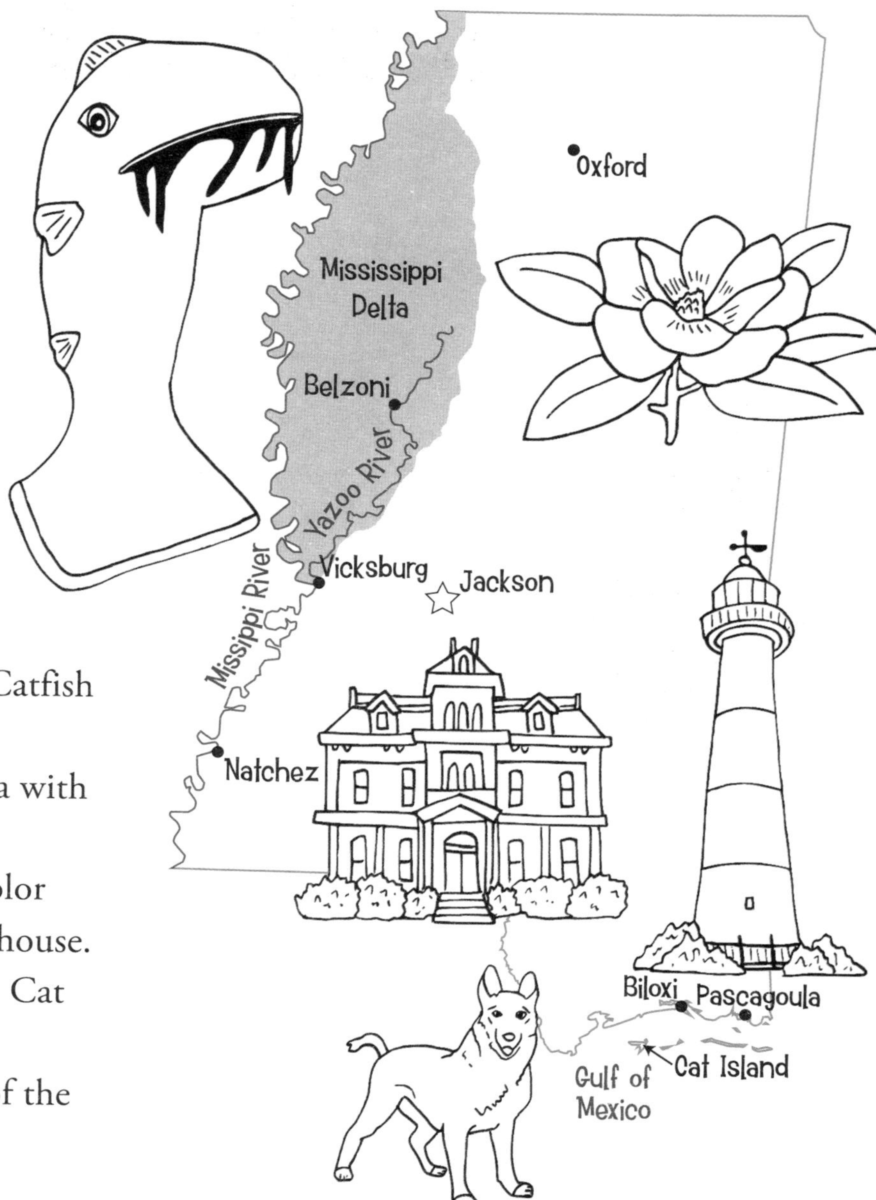

Magnolia

Mockingbird

In 2020 the Mississippi state government decided to change their state flag. The new design was not in place at the time this Atlas Workbook was published. If you would like to draw the new state flag, you may do so in the frame above.

South: Arkansas

Write the word **hot spring** on the blank. Trace over the faint lines and add your own details to illustrate a hot spring in Arkansas.

____

a spring that is naturally heated below the ground

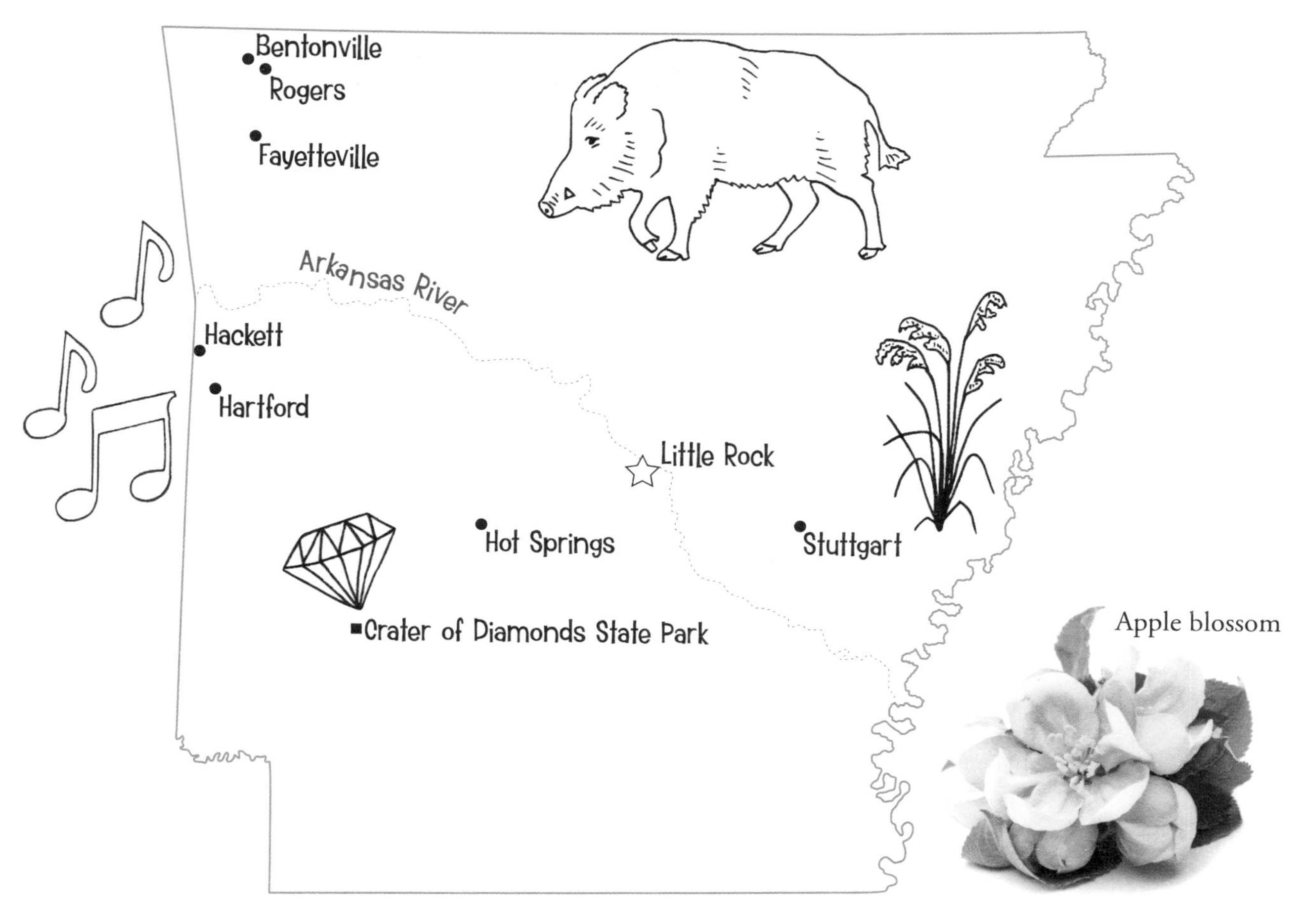

Apple blossom

1. Look at the state flag, bird, tree, and flower of Arkansas pictured on this page.
2. Color Arkansas red on the map on pages 2-3.
3. Color the star that marks Little Rock, the capital of Arkansas, yellow.
4. Color the wild hog (razorback) brown.
5. Draw more rice plants around Stuttgart.
6. Trace along the Arkansas River with blue.
7. Draw more diamonds around Crater of Diamonds State Park.
8. Color the music notes to represent the Hartford Music Company.

Pine

Mockingbird

South: Louisiana

Write the word **bayou** on the blank. Trace over the faint lines and add your own details to illustrate a bayou in Louisiana.

____

a swampy area in a river or lake
where the water is still
or a creek that moves along slowly

1. Look at the state flag, bird, tree, and flower of Louisiana pictured on this page.
2. Color Louisiana red on the map on pages 2-3.
3. Color the star that marks Baton Rouge, the capital of Louisiana, yellow.
4. Color the leaves green on the cypress tree growing out of Black Bayou Lake. Color the Spanish moss hanging from the branches gray. Color the trunk and the cypress knees brown. Cypress knees are growths of wood that grow up from the tree's roots.
5. Color the frog beside Rayne, the Frog Capital of the World.
6. Color the saxophone beside New Orleans gold. The saxophone is a common instrument used in jazz music.
7. Color Lake Pontchartrain blue.
8. Draw waves in the Gulf of Mexico.
9. Color the peppers that grow on Avery Island red with green stems.

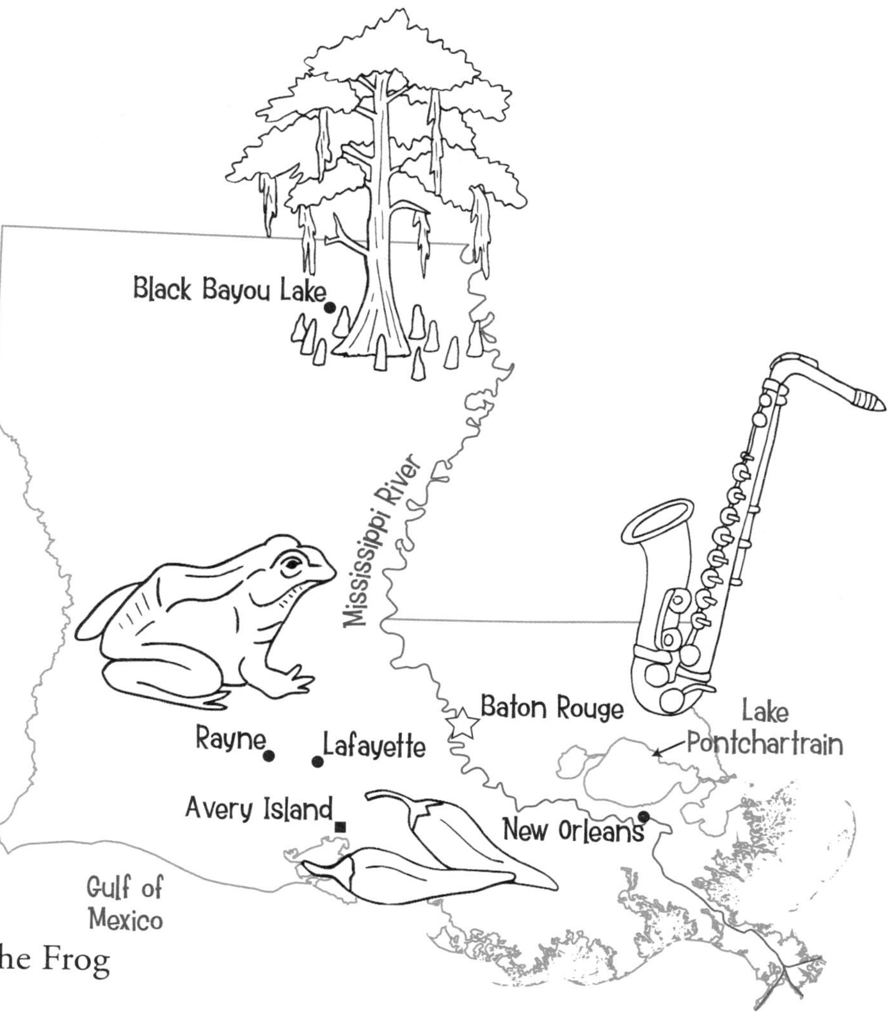

Bald cypress

Brown pelican

Magnolia

South: Florida

Write the words **barrier reef** on the blank. Trace over the faint lines and add your own details to illustrate the barrier reef near the Florida Keys.

____

an underwater ecosystem near a shoreline that is made by reef-building corals and is home to many sea creatures

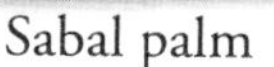

Sabal palm

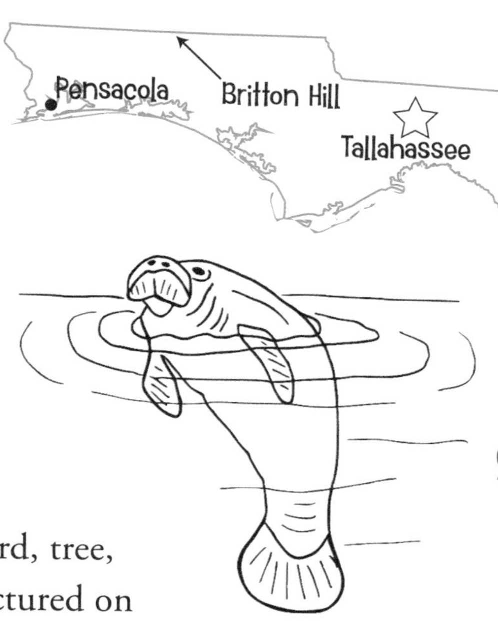

1. Look at the state flag, bird, tree, and flower of Florida pictured on this page.
2. Color Florida red on the map on pages 2-3.
3. Color the star that marks Tallahassee, the capital of Florida, yellow.
4. Color the oranges that will be made into orange juice, the official state drink of Florida.
5. Color the manatee enjoying the warm water of Manatee Springs State Park gray.
6. Color Lake Okeechobee blue.
7. Use bright colors to color the reef beside the Florida Keys.
8. Use bright colors to color the Seminole doll.

Mockingbird

Orange blossom

Midwest: Michigan

Write the word **archipelago** on the blank. Trace over the faint lines and add your own details to illustrate the part of the archipelago that makes up Isle Royale National Park.

____

a group of islands

1. Look at the state flag, bird, tree, and flower of Michigan pictured on this page.
2. Color Michigan purple on the map on pages 2-3.
3. Color the star that marks Lansing, the capital of Michigan, yellow.
4. Color Michigan's Upper Peninsula green.
5. Draw more snowflakes above the Upper Peninsula since places there receive such a large amount of snow.
6. Color the seaplane beside Isle Royale National Park.
7. Use brown to draw sand dunes at Silver Lake Sand Dunes.
8. Color the car beside Motor City (Detroit).

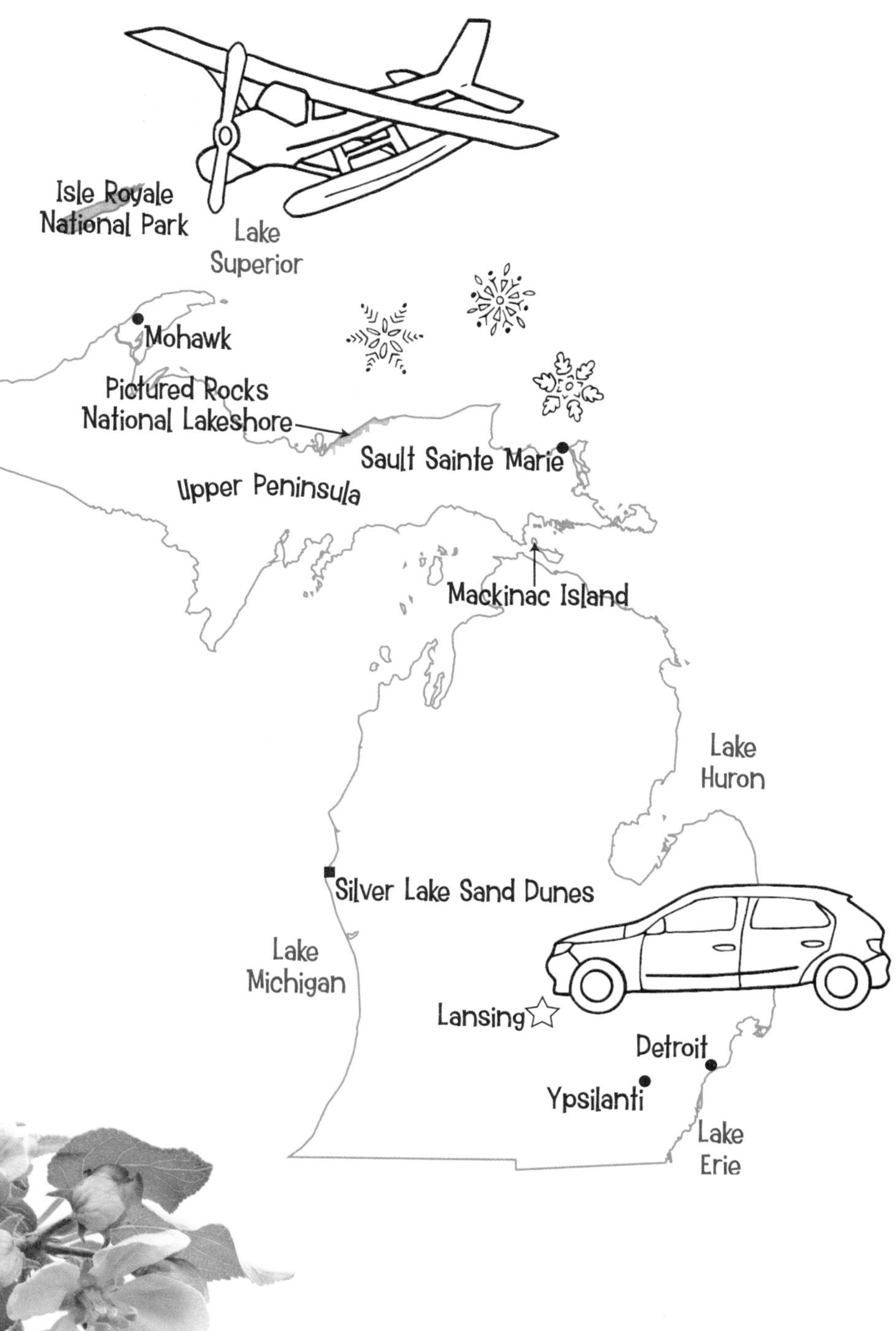

Apple blossom

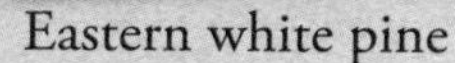

Eastern white pine

American robin

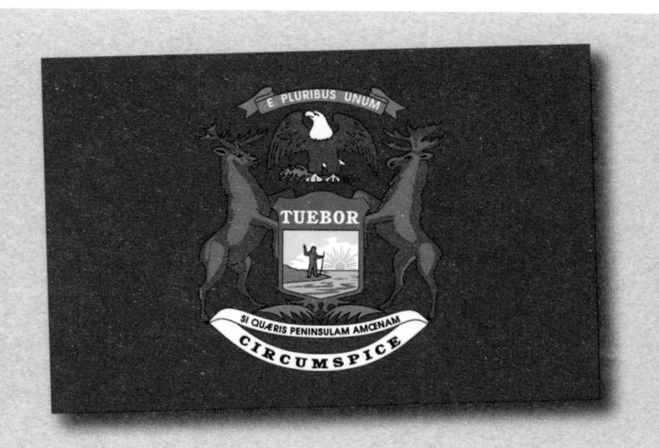

Midwest: Ohio

Write the words **vernal pool** on the blank. Trace over the faint lines and add your own details to illustrate salamander eggs in a vernal pool.

____

a seasonal pool of water
that dries up during part of the year

1. Look at the state flag, bird, tree, and flower of Ohio pictured on this page. The buckeye on the map shows what one looks like without a shell.
2. Color Ohio purple on the map on pages 2-3.
3. Color the star that marks Columbus, the capital of Ohio, yellow.

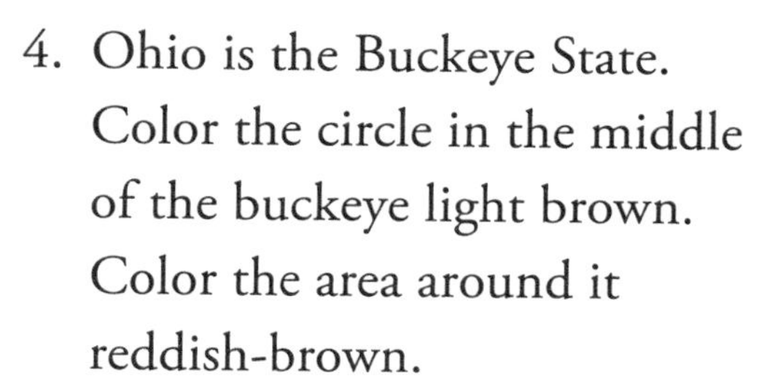

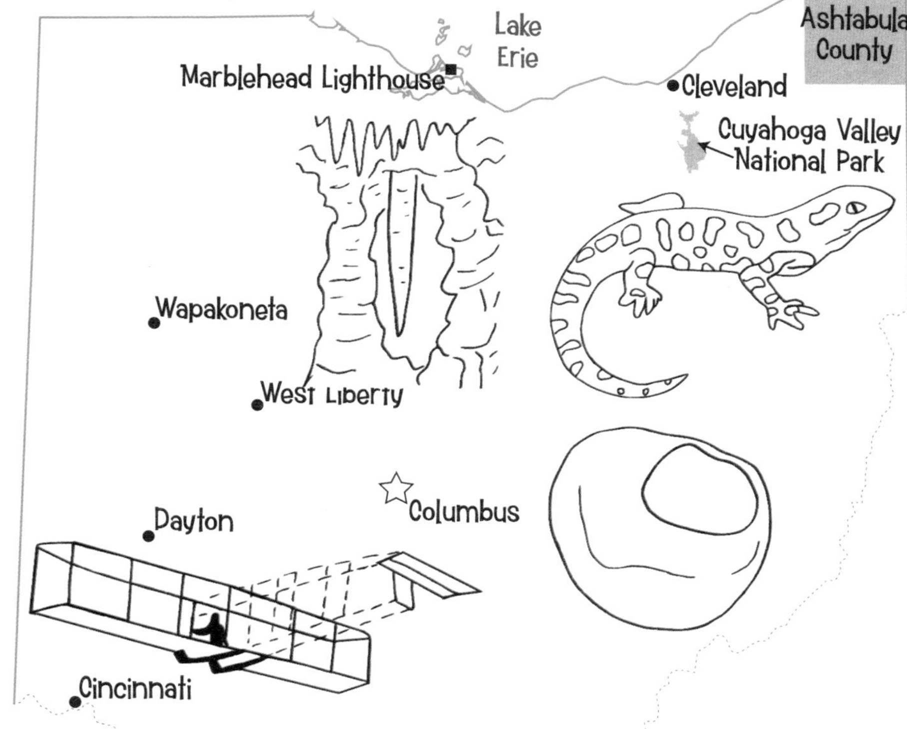

4. Ohio is the Buckeye State. Color the circle in the middle of the buckeye light brown. Color the area around it reddish-brown.
5. Color the Ashtabula County covered bridge to look like old wood.
6. Trace along the Ohio River with blue.
7. This salamander has just laid her eggs in a vernal pool in Cuyahoga Valley National Park. Color her dark gray with yellow spots.
8. Ohio is the Birthplace of Aviation. Draw over the dotted lines to complete the Wright Brothers' glider.
9. Use different shades of brown to color the Ohio Caverns formations around the Crystal King stalactite. Leave the Crystal King white.

Northern Cardinal

Ohio buckeye

Red carnation

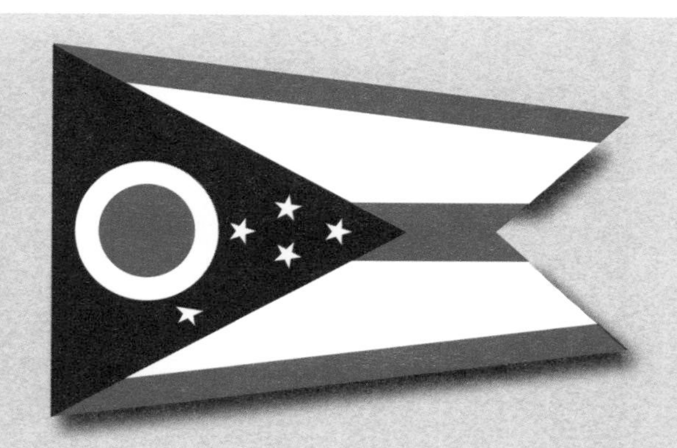

Midwest: Indiana

Write the word **bog** on the blank. Trace over the faint lines and add your own details to illustrate Pinhook Bog in Indiana.

____

ground that is wet and spongy

1. Look at the state flag, bird, tree, and flower of Indiana pictured on this page.
2. Color Indiana purple on the map on pages 2-3.
3. Color the star that marks Indianapolis, the capital of Indiana, yellow.
4. Draw more popcorn around the town of Popcorn.
5. Color the race car speeding around the track at the Indianapolis Motor Speedway in Indianapolis.
6. Indiana limestone is some of the strongest limestone in the world. Color it gray.
7. Color the walls of the hotel in West Baden Springs light yellow. Color the roof red.

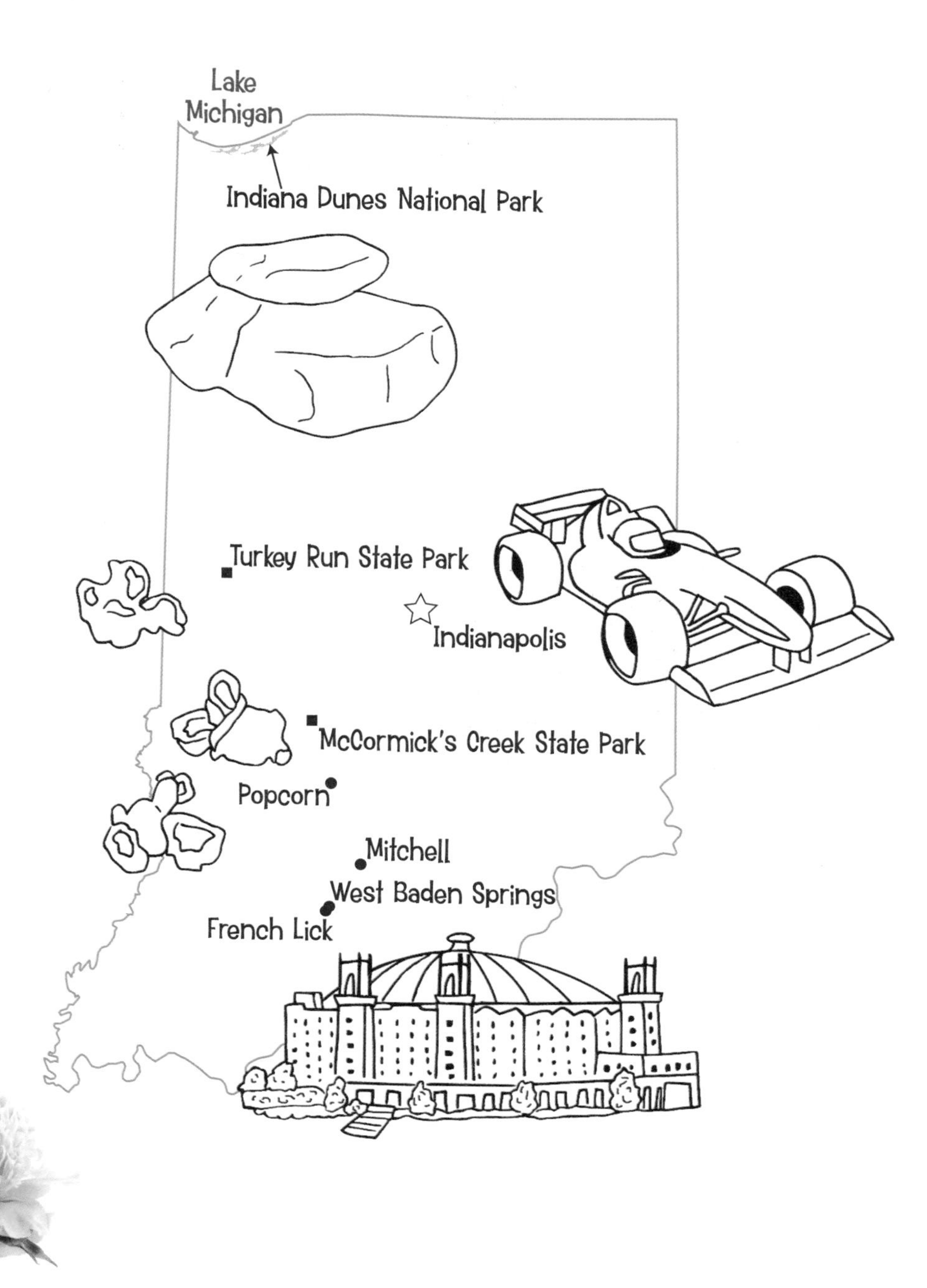

Peony

Northern Cardinal

Tulip tree

Midwest: Illinois

Write the word **prairie** on the blank. Trace over the faint lines and add your own details to illustrate a prairie. You can add a barn or a house or simply fill in the prairie with grasses and flowers.

____

a large open area of grassland

1. Look at the state flag, bird, tree, and flower of Illinois pictured on this page.
2. Color Illinois purple on the map on pages 2-3.
3. Color the star that marks Springfield, the capital of Illinois, yellow.
4. Color the corn yellow and the husk green. Color the soybeans beside the corn green.
5. Trace along the Mississippi River with blue.
6. Color Abraham Lincoln's hat beside Springfield black.
7. Draw three trees in the Shawnee National Forest.
8. Draw a tall building beside Chicago.
9. Color the mining truck between Peoria and Decatur yellow.

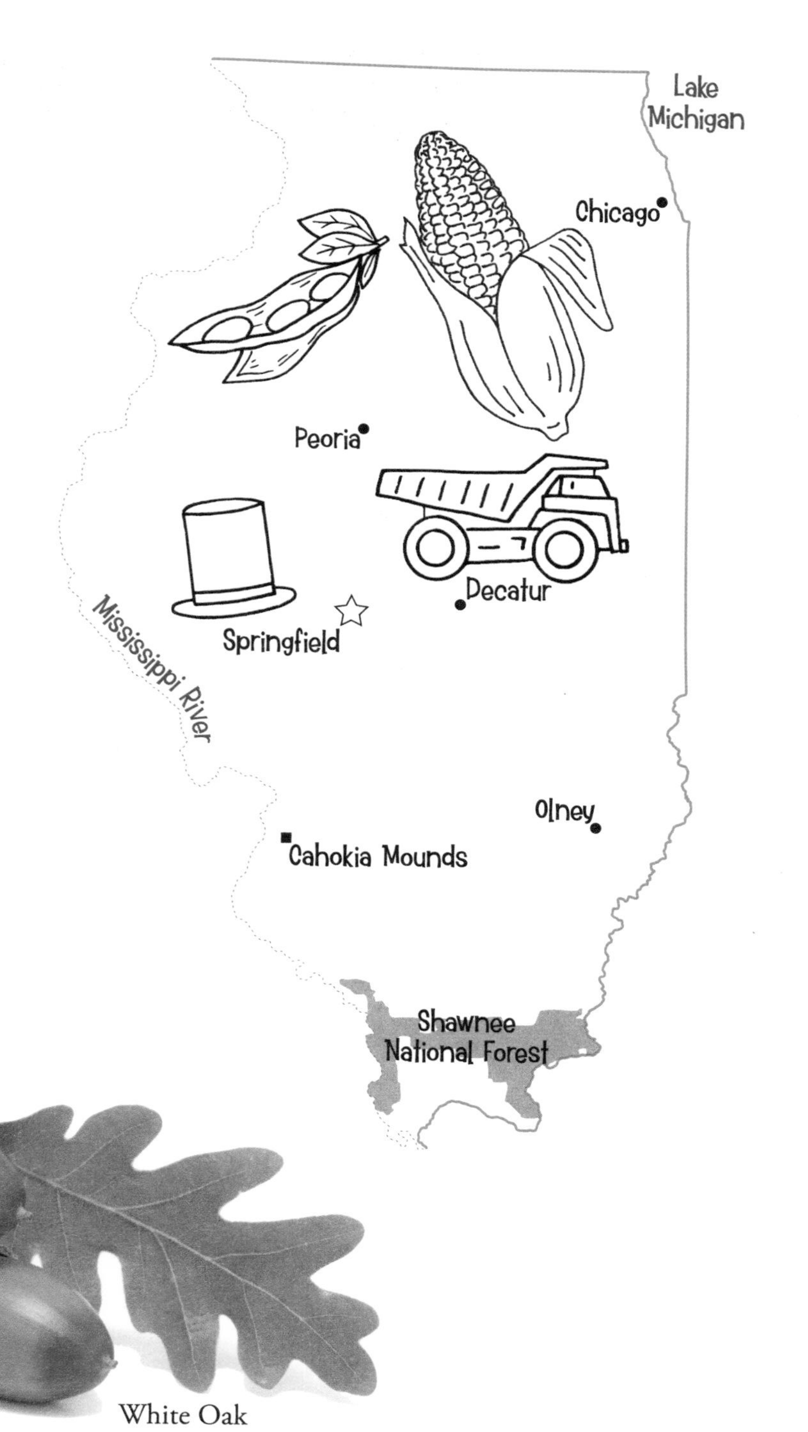

White Oak

Northern cardinal

Violet

Midwest: Wisconsin

Write the word **isthmus** on the blank. Trace over the faint lines and add your own details to illustrate the isthmus in Madison. (You don't have to draw all the buildings, but draw a few, including the capitol.)

____

a narrow strip of land with water on each side that connects two larger areas of land

1. Look at the state flag, bird, tree, and flower of Wisconsin pictured on this page.
2. Color Wisconsin purple on the map on pages 2-3.
3. Color the star that marks Madison, the capital of Wisconsin, yellow.
4. Color the football beside Green Bay, the home of the Green Bay Packers football team.
5. Color the Door Peninsula green.
6. Color the cherries beside the Door Peninsula red. Imagine the ten million pounds of cherries that grow there every year!

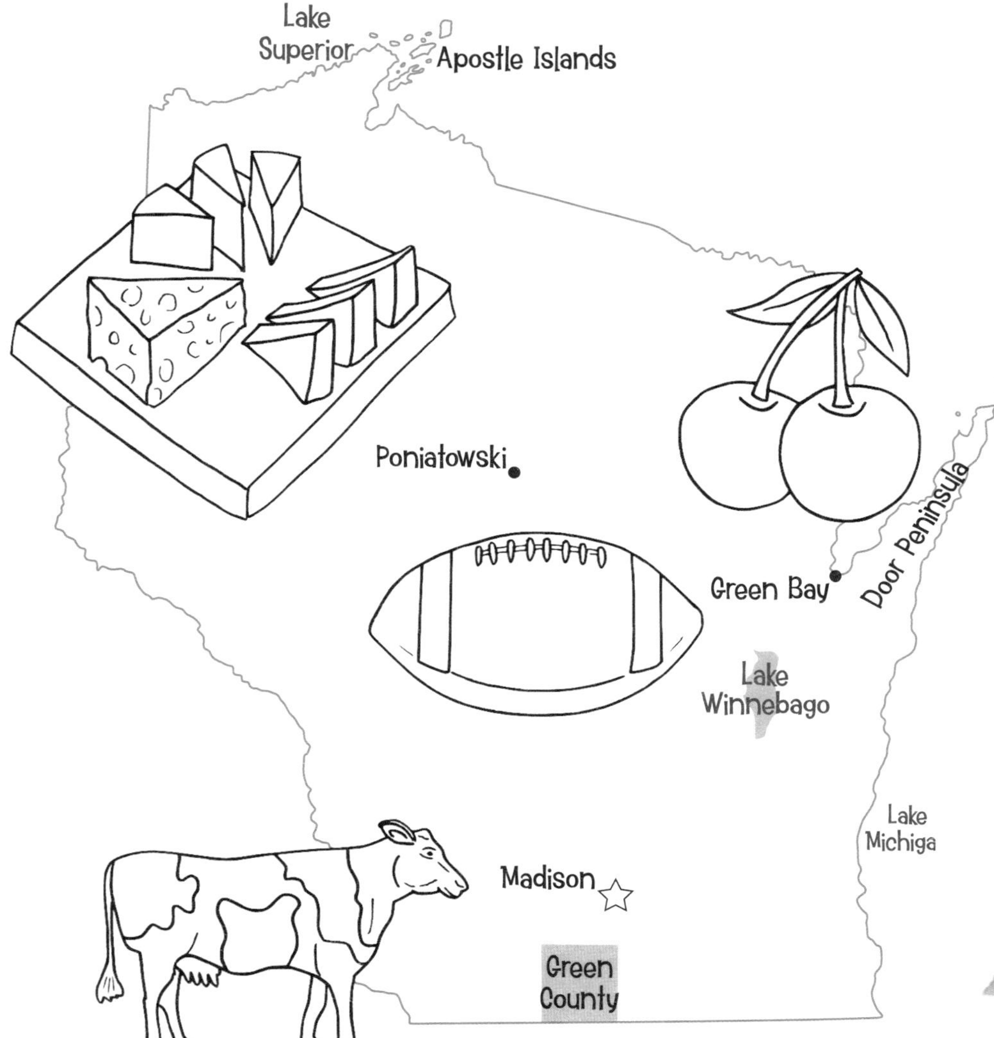

7. Wisconsin produces more cheese than any other state. Color the cheese different shades of yellow and orange. Leave the swiss cheese (the piece with holes) white.
8. Color the spots black on the dairy cow that helped supply Casper Jaggi's factory with milk.

Wood violets

Sugar maple

American robin

Midwest: Minnesota

Write the word **reservation** on the blank. Trace over the faint lines and add the other details to illustrate the logo of the White Earth Reservation in Minnesota.

____

an area of land
managed by a native nation

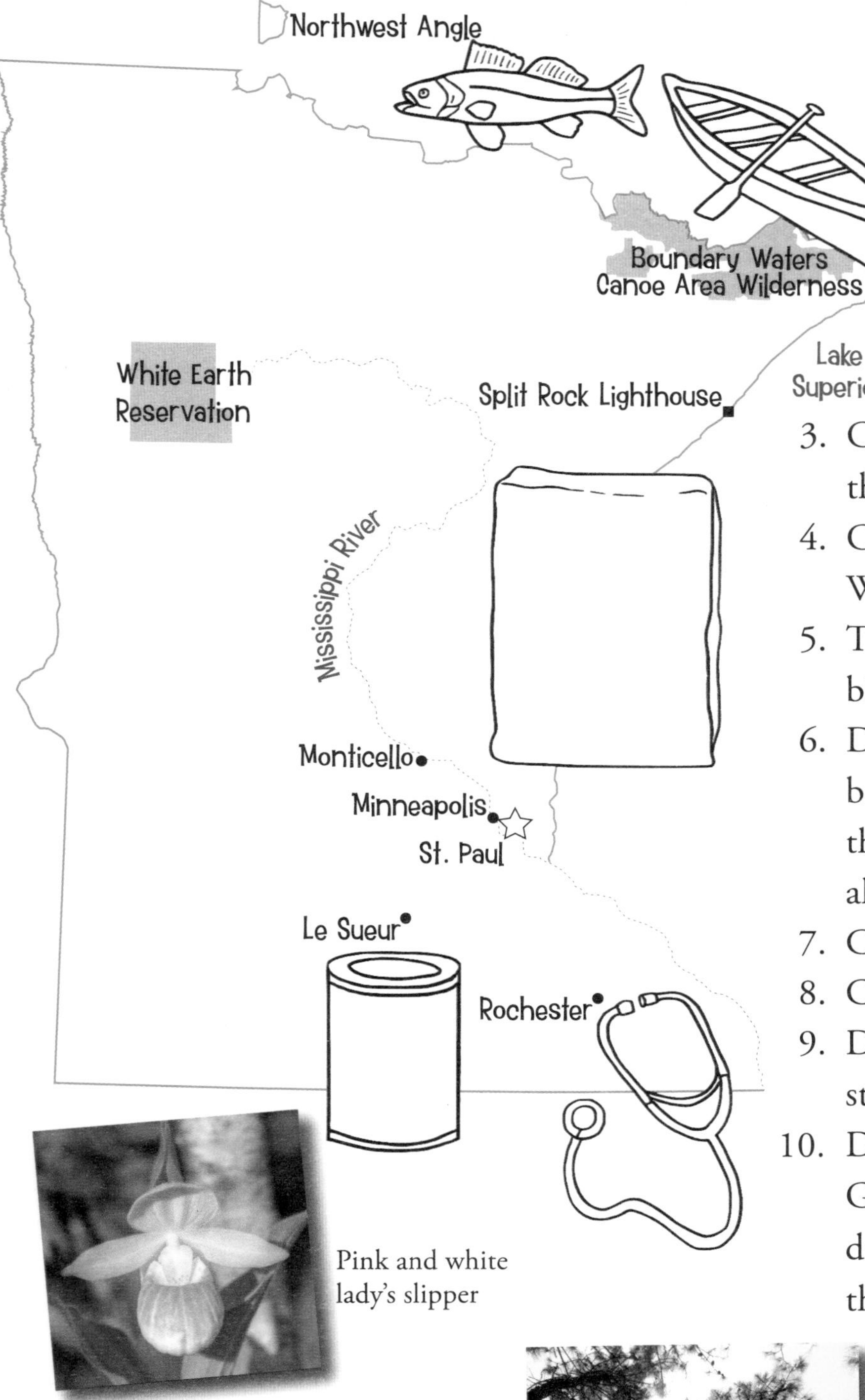

1. Look at the [illegible] flag, bird, tree, [illegible] flower of Minnesota pictured on this page.
2. Color Minnesota purple on the map on pages 2-3.
3. Color the star that marks St. Paul, the capital of Minnesota, yellow.
4. Color the canoe in the Boundary Waters Canoe Area Wilderness.
5. Trace along the Mississippi with blue.
6. Draw a design on the bag of flour beside Minneapolis, which earned the nickname Mill City because of all the flour once produced there.
7. Color the Northwest Angle green.
8. Color the walleye fish light brown.
9. Draw a heart beside Dr. Mayo's stethoscope.
10. Draw two more cans packaged by the Green Giant company. On each can, draw a picture or write the name of the vegetable that is inside.

Pink and white lady's slipper

Common loon

Red pine

Midwest: Iowa

Write the word **rural** on the blank. Trace over the faint lines and add your own details to illustrate a barn in Iowa. Use a ruler to finish the lines on the roof. Are there any animals in your barnyard?

____

in the countryside,
outside of a city or town

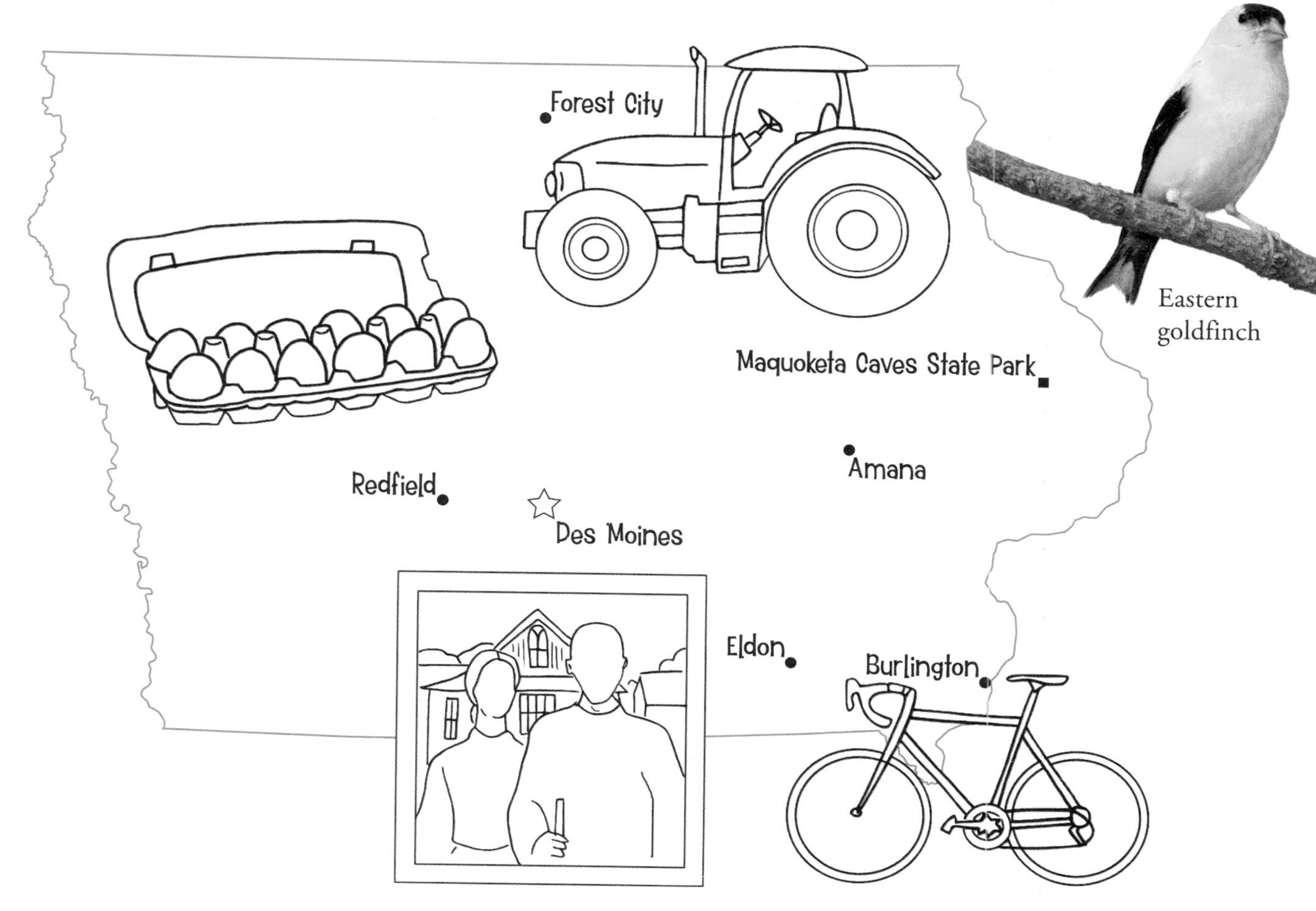

1. Look at the state flag, bird, tree, and flower of Iowa pictured on this page.
2. Color Iowa purple on the map on pages 2-3.
3. Color the star that marks Des Moines, the capital of Iowa, yellow.
4. Iowa chickens produce more eggs than the chickens in any other state. Color the egg carton.
5. Many people in Iowa live a rural farming lifestyle. Color the tractor.
6. Use your imagination and turn the painting next to Eldon into your own silly version of *American Gothic*. Will the man be holding a pitchfork, or something else?
7. Color the bicycle and imagine riding it up Snake Alley 25 times!

Oak

Wild rose

Midwest: Missouri

Write the word **tor** on the blank. Trace over the faint lines and add your own details to illustrate the Elephant Rocks tor in Missouri.

____

a mass of rocks that lies in the open on the top of a hill

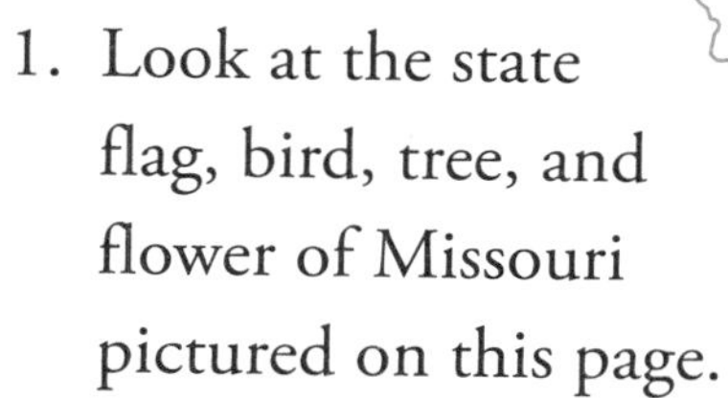

1. Look at the state flag, bird, tree, and flower of Missouri pictured on this page.
2. Color Missouri purple on the map on pages 2-3.
3. Color the star that marks Jefferson City, the capital of Missouri, yellow.
4. Color the sliced bread beside Chillicothe, the Home of Sliced Bread.
5. Color the Gateway Arch over St. Louis gray.
6. Color the Missouri Bootheel green.
7. Draw small rounded mountains throughout the Ozark Mountains.
8. Color the Baldknobbers' washboard beside Branson. Color the wooden frame brown and the center metal area gray. Color the music notes coming from it.
9. Draw a design on the wrapping paper and the greeting card beside Kansas City, the home of Hallmark.

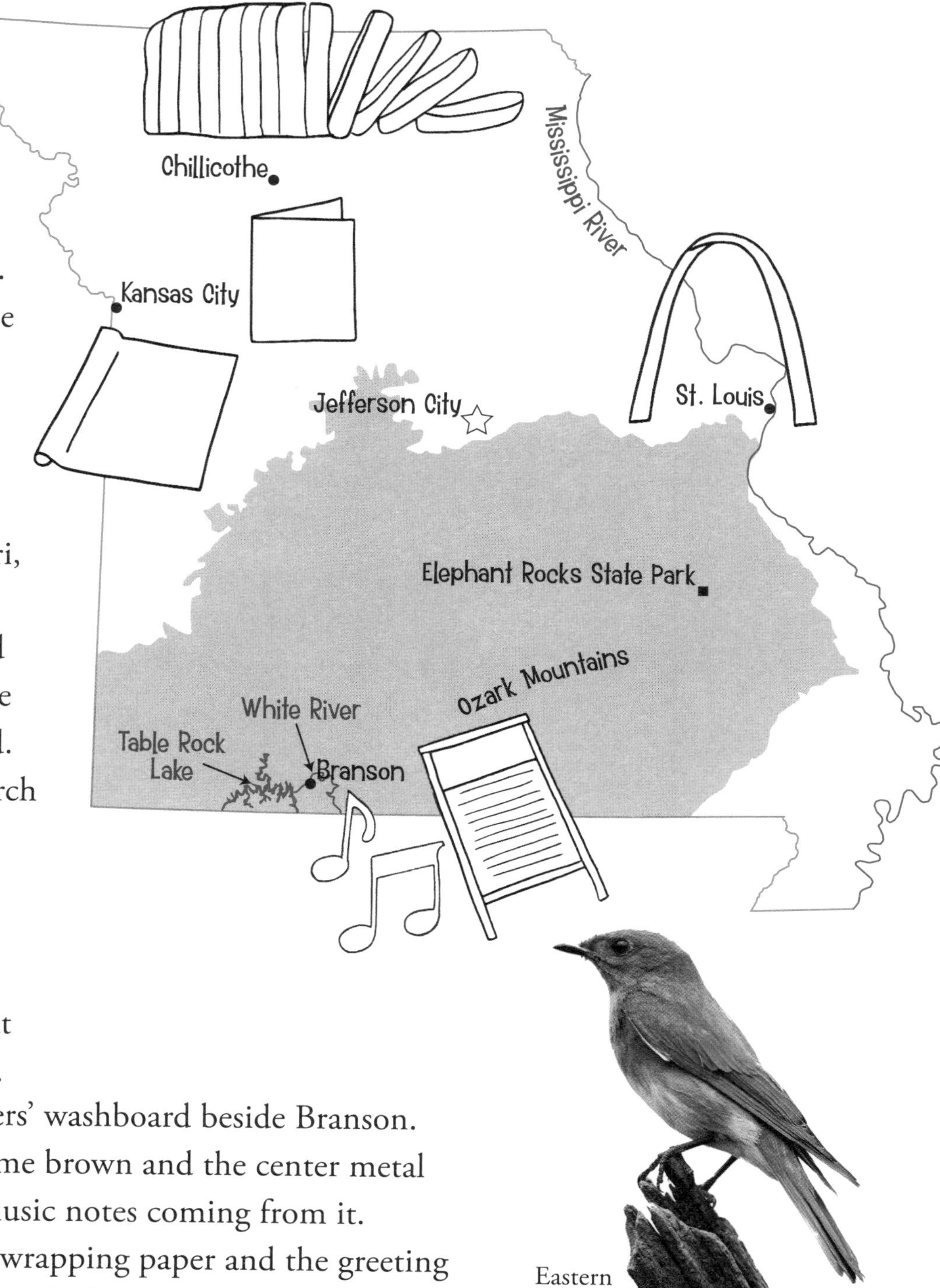

Eastern bluebird

White hawthorn blossom

Flowering dogwood

Midwest: Kansas

Write the word **concretion** on the blank. Trace over the faint lines and add your own details to illustrate a concretion in Kansas. Add shading to your drawing to match the shadows in the photograph.

____

a hard body of rock cemented with a mineral, often forming a round shape

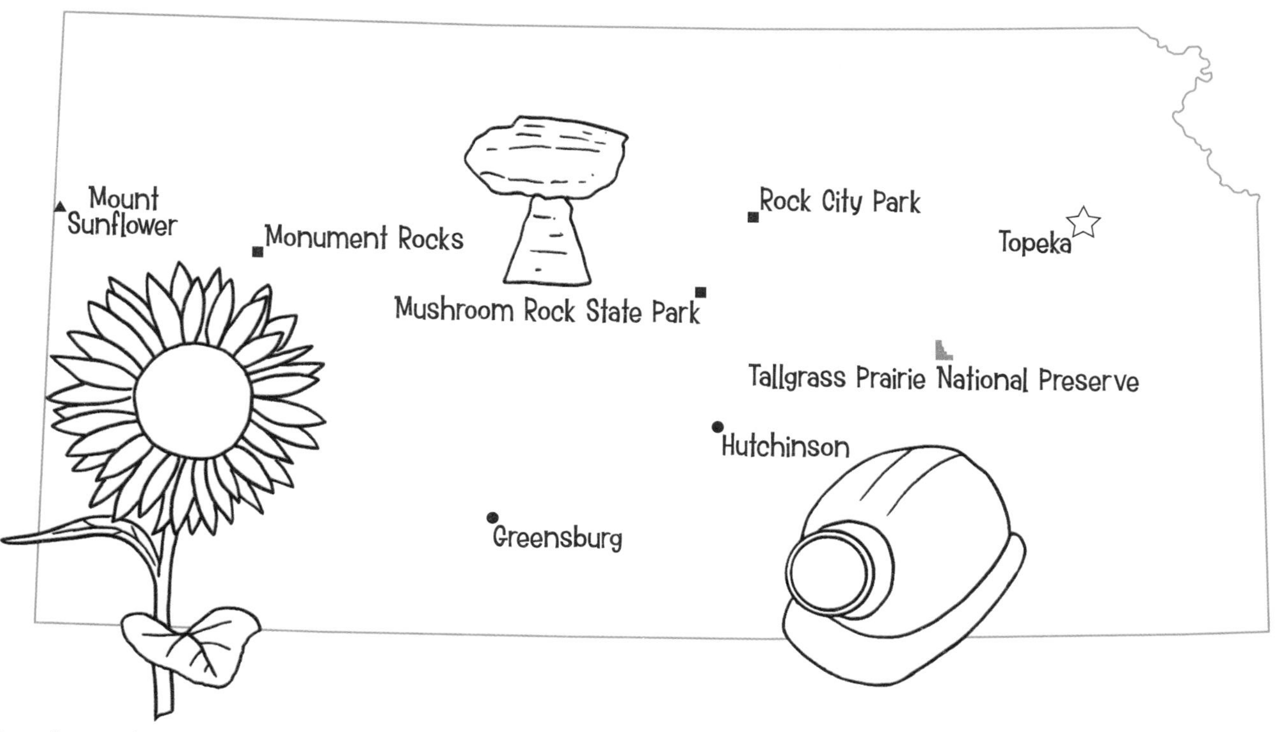

1. Look at the state flag, bird, tree, and flower of Kansas pictured on this page.
2. Color Kansas purple on the map on pages 2-3.
3. Color the star that marks Topeka, the capital of Kansas, yellow.
4. Draw prairie grass around the shape that marks the Tallgrass Prairie National Preserve.
5. Choose a color for the salt mining hard hat beside Hutchinson. Color the light on the hat yellow.
6. Draw two more mushroom rocks around Mushroom Rocks State Park. Use gray and brown to color them.
7. Color the sunflower beside Mount Sunflower, the highest point in Kansas. Color the center brown, the petals yellow, and the leaves and stem green.

Western meadowlark

Cottonwood

Wild native sunflower

Midwest: Nebraska

Write the word **excavation** on the blank. Trace over the faint lines and add your own details to illustrate the excavation of a fossil site. Add more some fossils on the ground.

____

a careful dig in a certain area

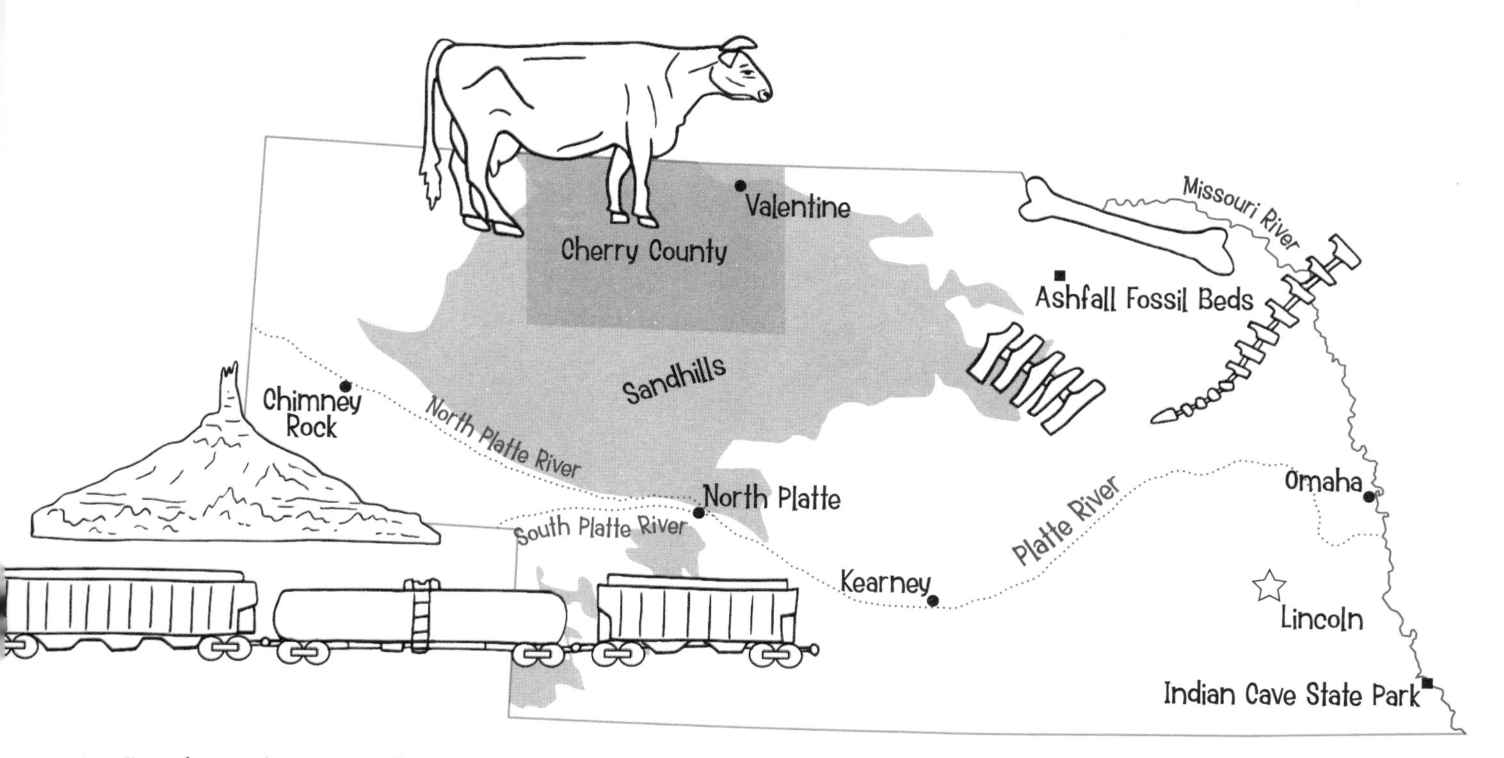

1. Look at the state flag, bird, tree, and flower of Nebraska pictured on this page.
2. Color Nebraska purple on the map on pages 2-3.
3. Color the star that marks Lincoln, the capital of Nebraska, yellow.
4. Draw small rounded hills throughout the Sandhills.
5. Cherry County has more cattle than any other county in the country. Trace around Cherry County with green. Color the cow brown.
6. The North and South Platte Rivers join to form the Platte River. Trace along these rivers with blue.
7. Color the train cars headed to Bailey Yard in North Platte, the busiest train yard in the world.
8. Color Chimney Rock brown.
9. Draw more fossil bones around Ashfall Fossil Beds.
10. Draw hearts around Valentine.

Western meadowlark

Cottonwood

Goldenrod

Midwest: South Dakota

Write the words **artesian well** on the blank. Trace over the faint lines and add your own details to illustrate Capitol Lake in Pierre, South Dakota, which is fed by an artesian well. Make sure you draw the capitol's reflection in the water.

____

a well with natural underground pressure

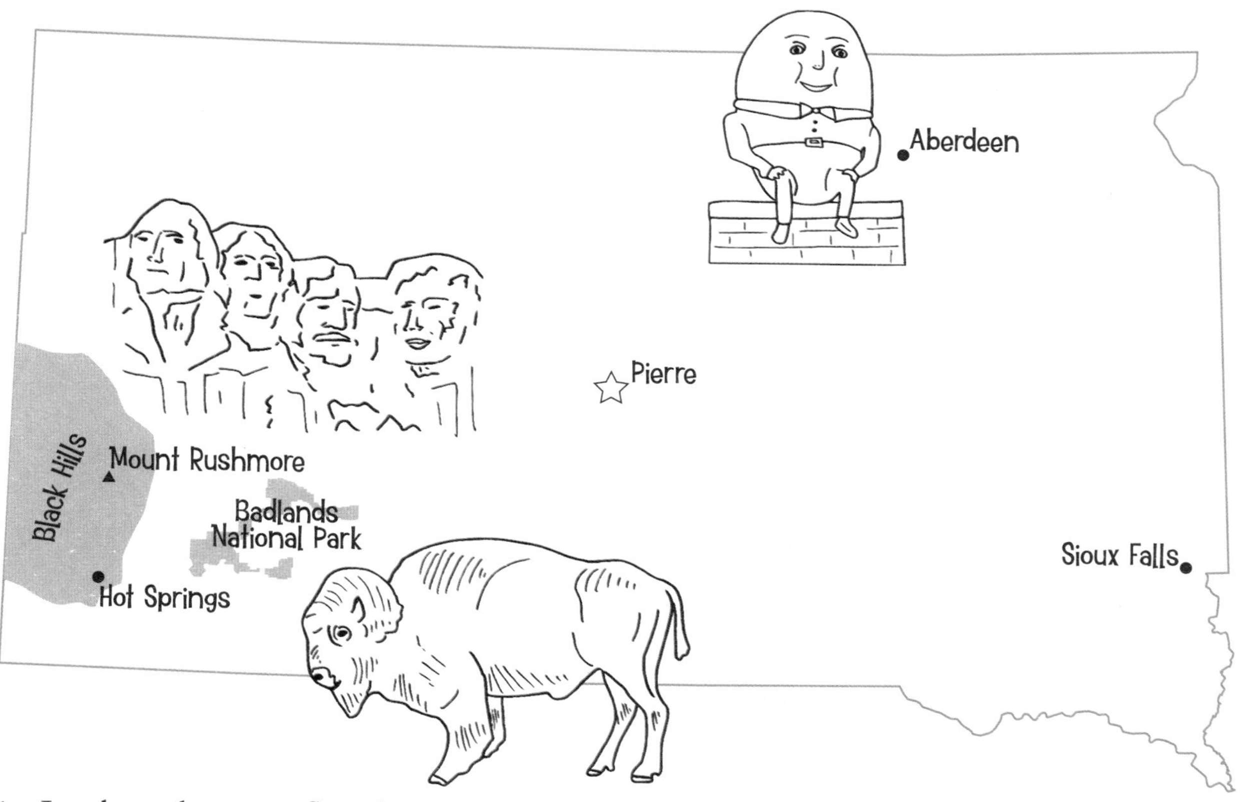

1. Look at the state flag, bird, tree, and flower of South Dakota pictured on this page.
2. Color South Dakota purple on the map on pages 2-3.
3. Color the star that marks Pierre, the capital of South Dakota, yellow.
4. Color Mount Rushmore gray.
5. Color the American bison in Badlands National Park brown.
6. Color the Humpty Dumpty statue at Storybook Land in Aberdeen. Color his shirt orange, his pants blue, and his shoes and bow tie red.

Ring-necked pheasant

Black Hills spruce

American pasque

Midwest: North Dakota

Write the word **butte** on the blank. Trace over the faint lines and add your own details to illustrate a butte in Theodore Roosevelt National Park.

____

a steep rocky hill that is mostly flat on top

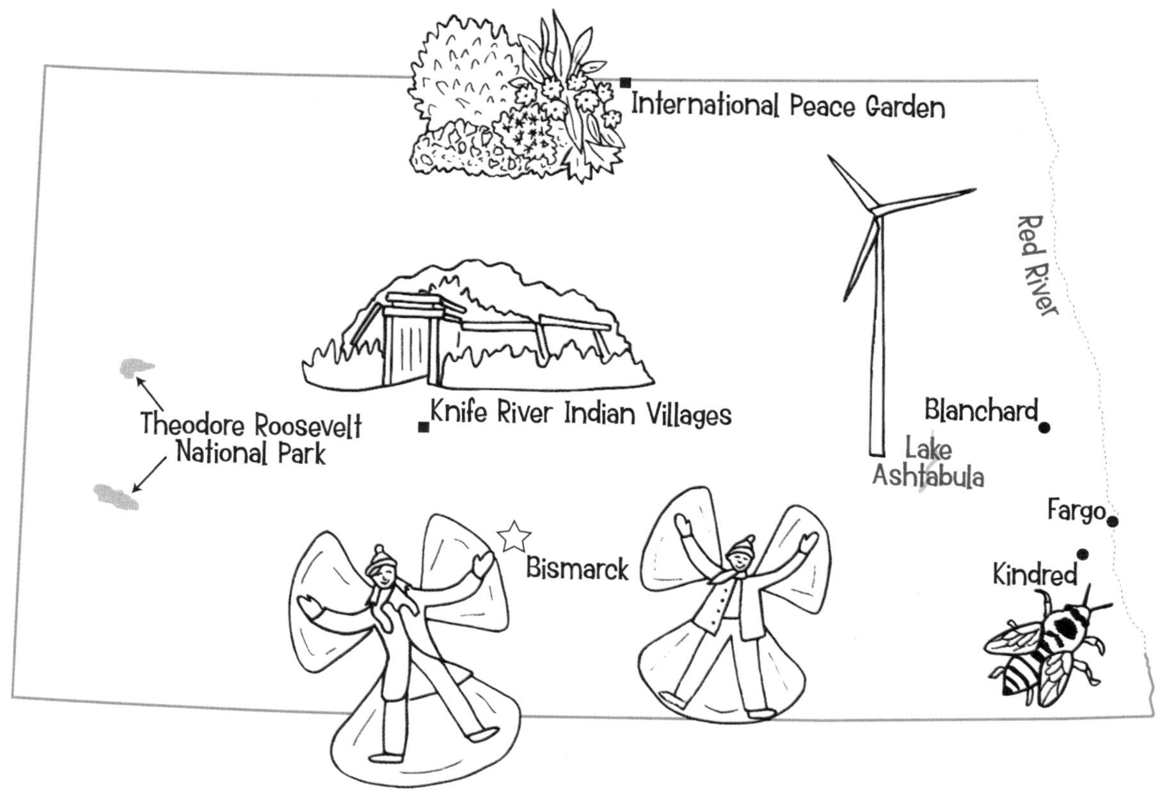

1. Look at the state flag, bird, tree, and flower of North Dakota pictured on this page.
2. Color North Dakota purple on the map on pages 2-3.
3. Color the star that marks Bismarck, the capital of North Dakota, yellow.
4. Draw more wind turbines around Lake Ashtabula.
5. Trace along the Red River with blue.
6. Color the people helping to set a snow angel record beside the North Dakota State Capitol in 2007.
7. Color the earthlodge brown. Color the grasses growing up around it green.
8. Color the flowers in the International Peace Garden on the border with Canada.
9. Color Mark Sperry's honey bee yellow. Leave its wings white.

Western meadowlark

Wild prairie rose

American elm

Rocky Mountains: Montana

Write the word **glacier** on the blank. Trace over the faint lines and add your own details to illustrate Piegan Glacier in Montana.

____

a mass of ice on land that moves very slowly as a result of gravity and its own weight

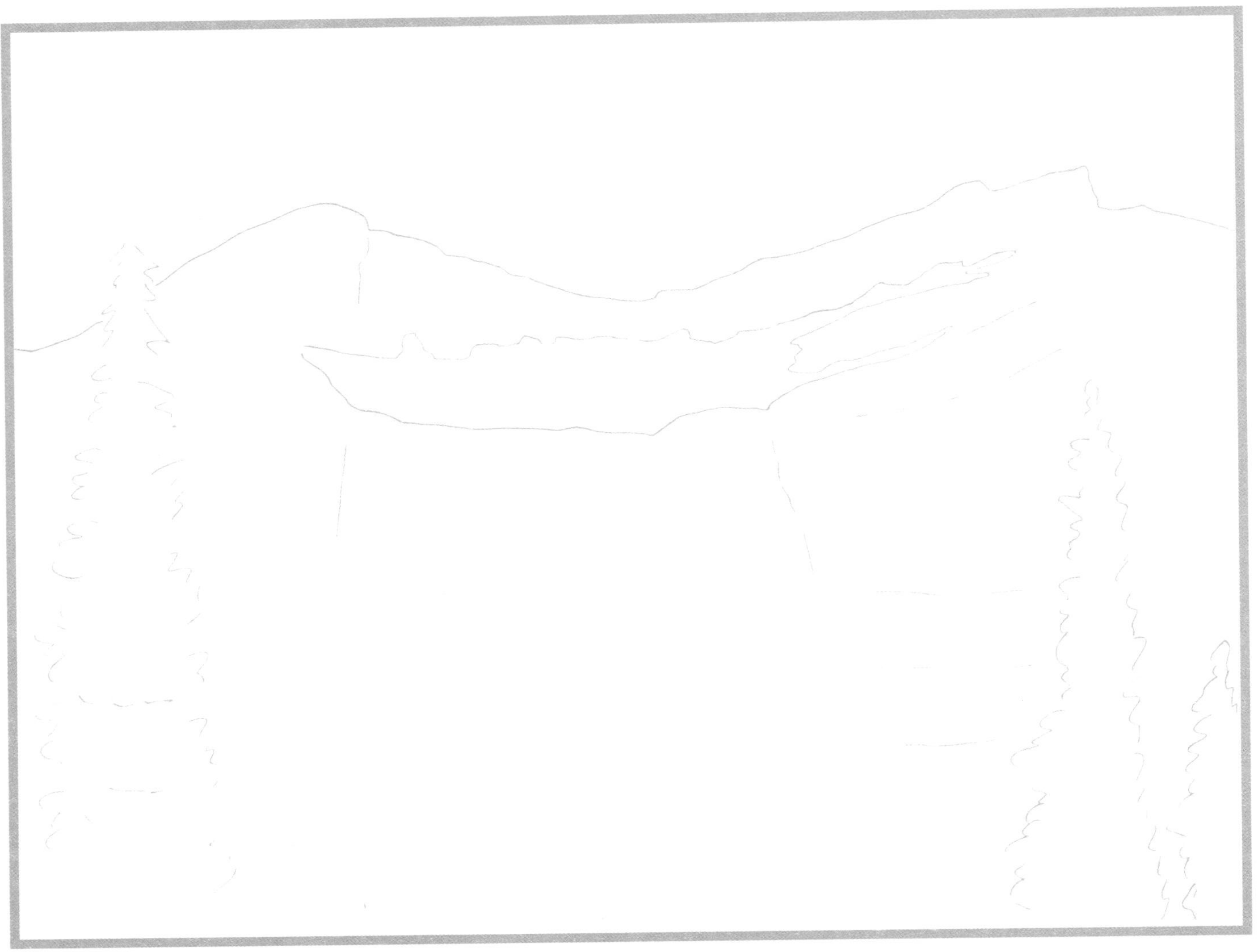

1. Look at the state flag, bird, tree, and flower of Montana pictured on this page.
2. Color Montana blue on the map on pages 2-3.

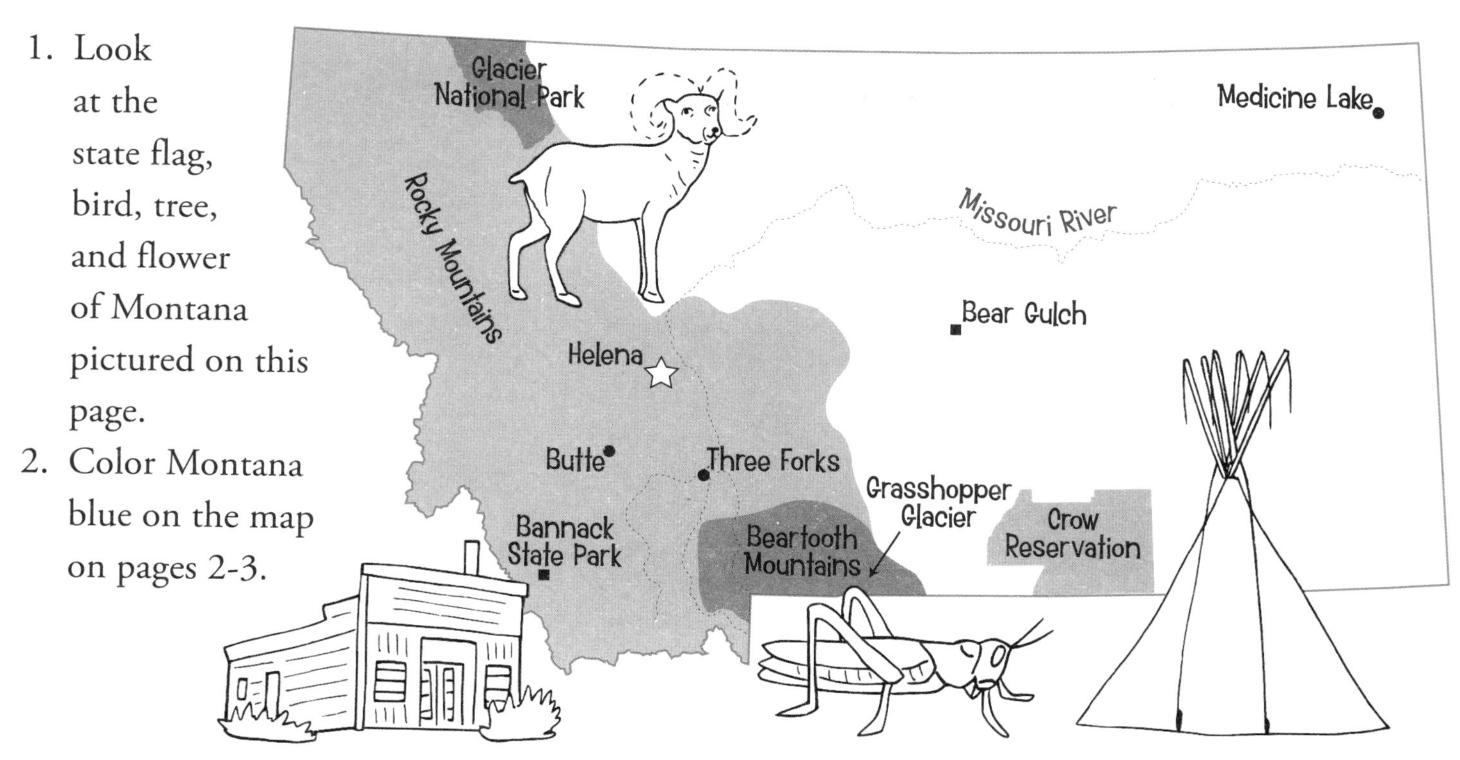

3. Color the star that marks Helena, the capital of Montana, yellow.
4. Trace along the three rivers that meet at Three Forks with blue. Also trace along the Missouri River, which begins at Three Forks, with blue.
5. Draw a design on the teepee. Today the Crow people live in modern houses, but the teepee is the traditional Crow dwelling.
6. Color the grasshopper below Grasshopper Glacier green.
7. Color the abandoned building in the ghost town of Bannack brown.
8. Draw mountains in the area labeled Rocky Mountains.
9. Trace over the horns of the bighorn sheep beside Glacier National Park.

Ponderosa pine

Bitterroot

Western meadowlark

Rocky Mountains: Idaho

Write the word **dune** on the blank. Trace over the faint lines and add your own details to illustrate the Bruneau Dunes in Idaho. Use shading or different colors to show how the light is shining on them.

____

a hill of sand formed by the wind, usually on the coast or in a desert

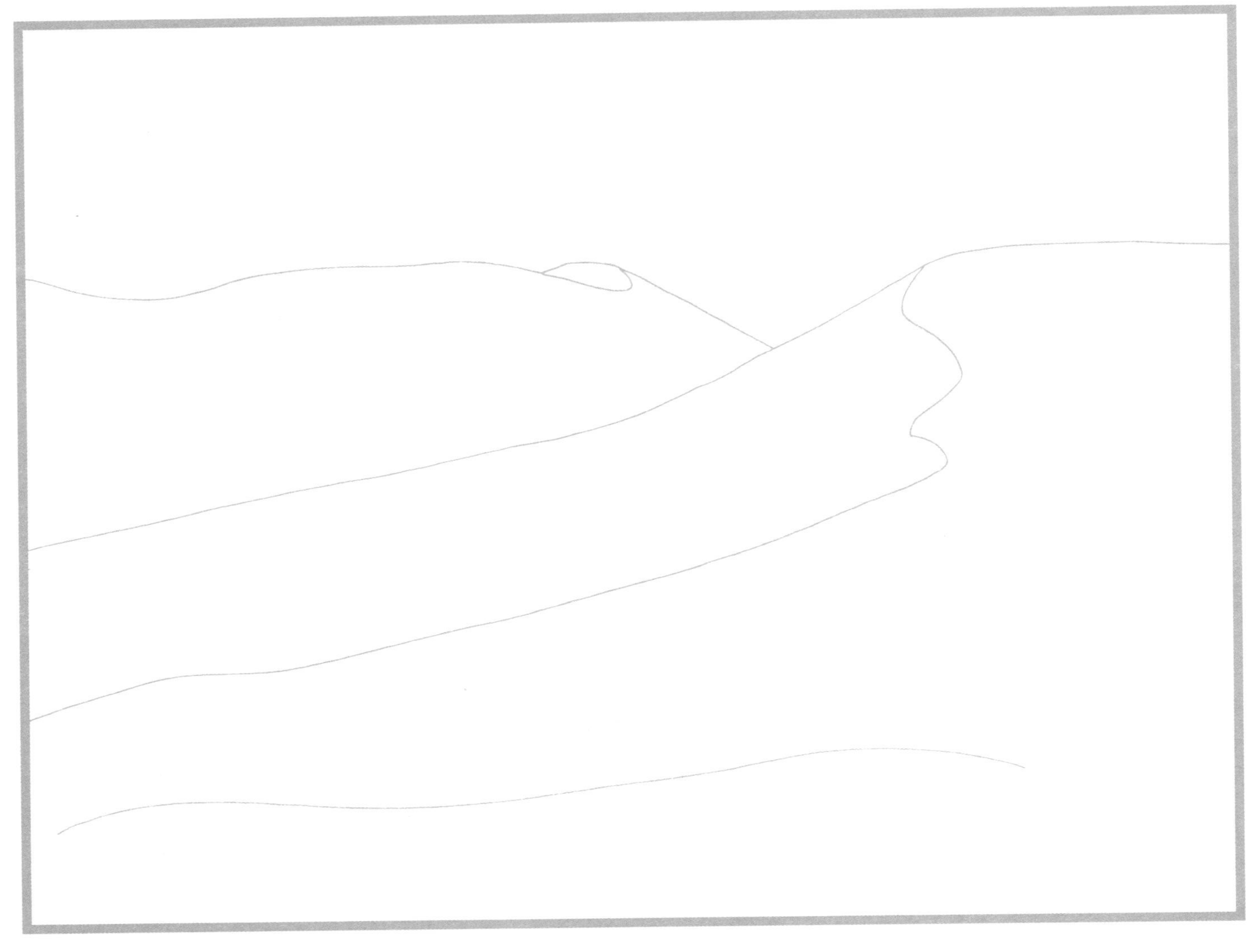

1. Look at the state flag, bird, tree, and flower of Idaho pictured on this page.
2. Color Idaho blue on the map on pages 2-3.
3. Color the star that marks Boise, the capital of Idaho, yellow.
4. Idaho is the Gem State. Fill the opal (the oval shape) with dots of many different colors.
5. More potatoes grow in Idaho than in any other state. Color the potatoes brown.
6. Trace along the Snake River with blue.
7. Color the person sandboarding at Bruneau Dunes.
8. Draw a tree beside Boise, the City of Trees.
9. Color the skier enjoying the slopes in Sun Valley.

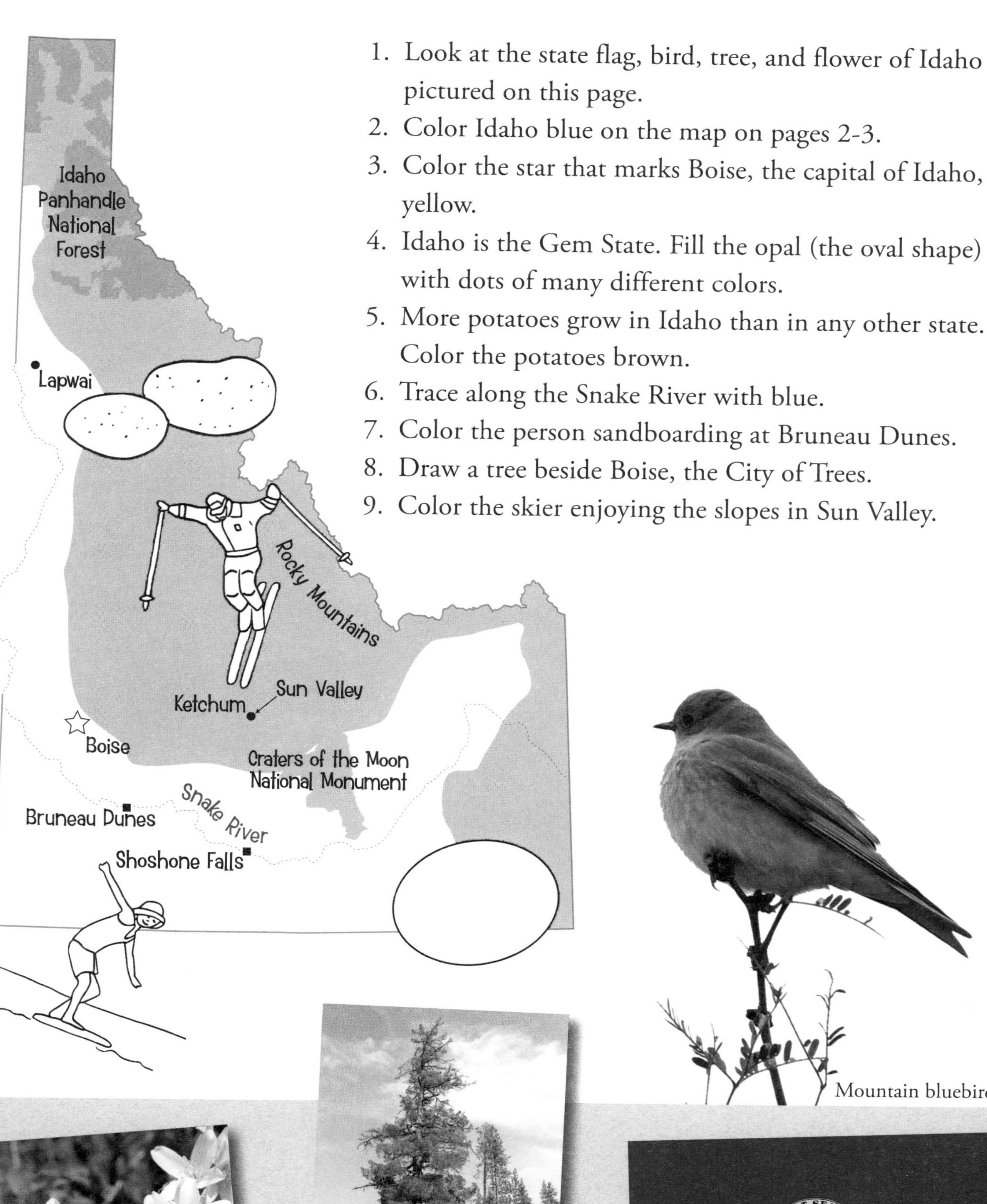

Mountain bluebird

Syringa

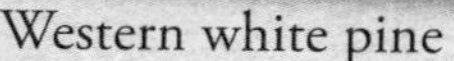
Western white pine

Rocky Mountains: Wyoming

Write the words **hydrothermal feature** on the blank. Trace over the faint lines and add your own details to illustrate the Grand Morning Glory Pool, a hydrothermal feature in Yellowstone.

____

a place where hot water
comes out of the earth

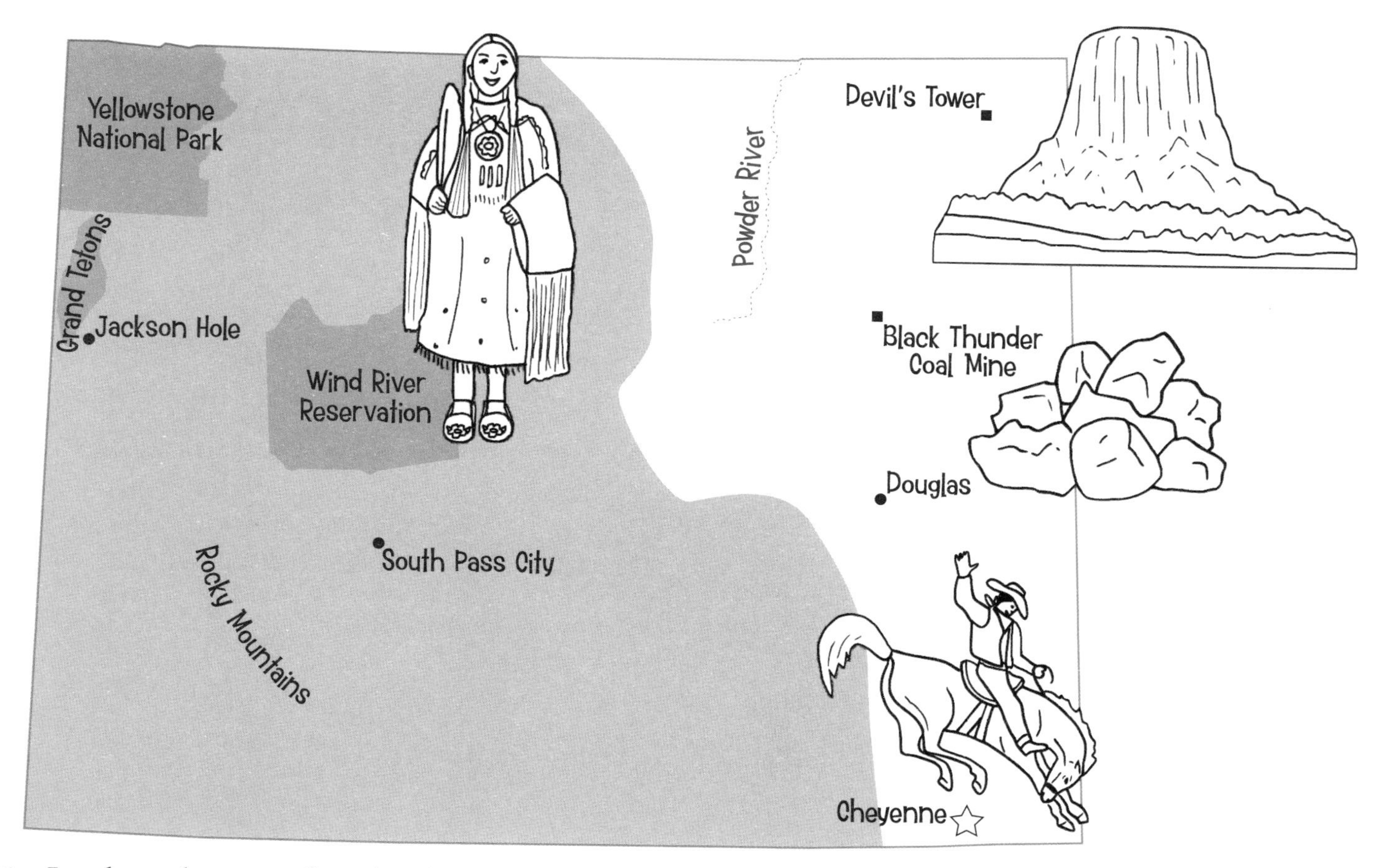

1. Look at the state flag, bird, tree, and flower of Wyoming pictured on this page.
2. Color Wyoming blue on the map on pages 2-3.
3. Color the star that marks Cheyenne, the capital of Wyoming, yellow.
4. Color Devil's Tower gray and the trees around its base green.
5. Trace along the Powder River with blue.
6. Color the pieces of coal mined in Wyoming black.
7. Color the cowboy and the bucking bronco the colors of your choice.
8. Color the Eastern Shoshone girl from the Wind River Reservation in her traditional costume.
9. Trace around the part of Yellowstone National Park that is in Wyoming with green.

Meadowlark

Plains cottonwood

Indian paintbrush

Rocky Mountains: Colorado

Write the word **canyon** on the blank. Trace over the faint lines and add your own details to illustrate the Black Canyon in Colorado.

____

a narrow deep valley with steep sides

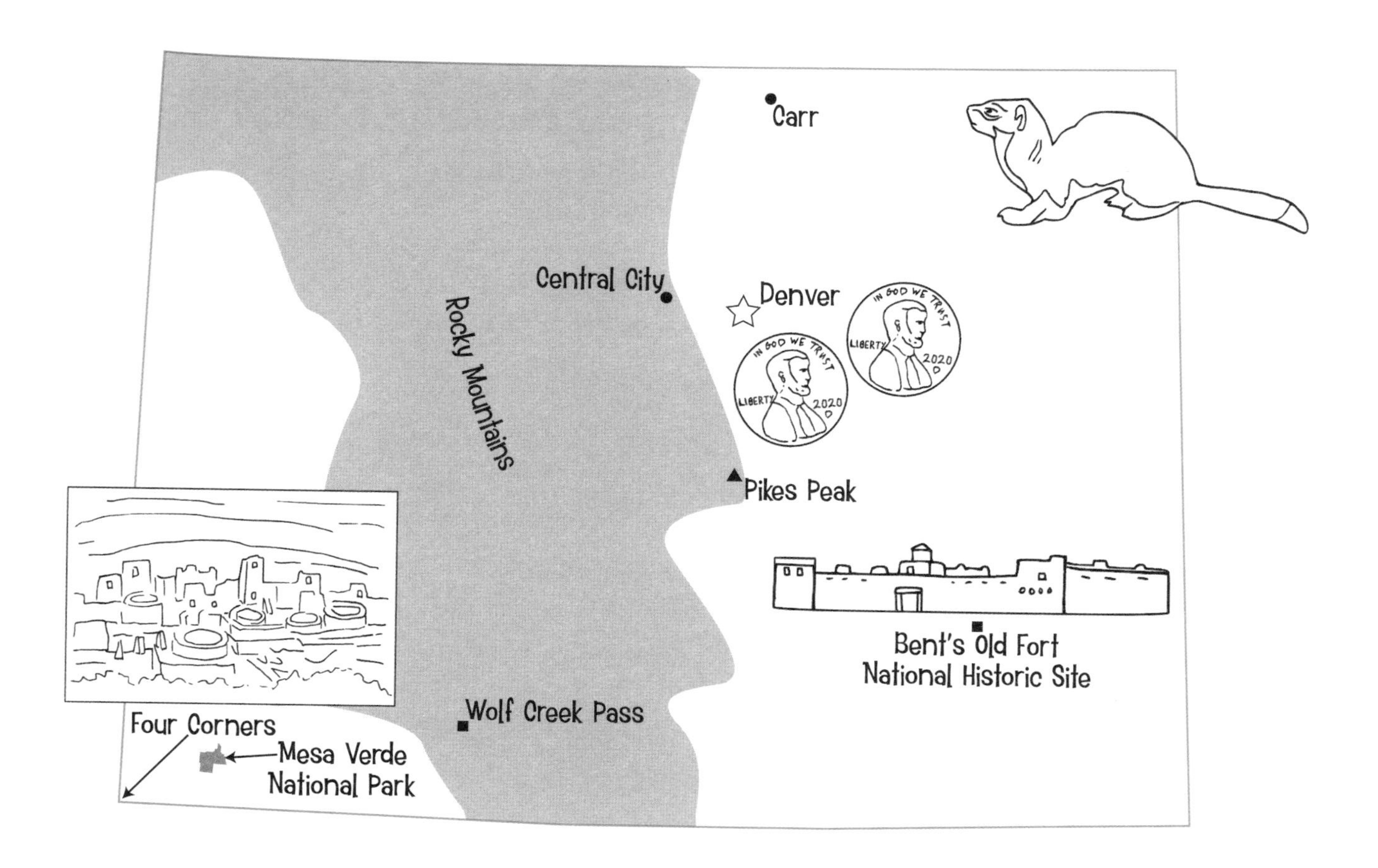

1. Look at the state flag, bird, tree, and flower of Colorado pictured on this page.
2. Color Colorado blue on the map on pages 2-3.
3. Color the star that marks Denver, the capital of Colorado, yellow.
4. Color the endangered black-footed ferret light brown. Color his feet, the area around his eye, and the tip of his tail black.
5. Color the pennies made at the Denver Mint copper (reddish brown).
6. Color Bent's Old Fort light brown
7. Color Mesa Verde light brown.
8. Draw mountains in the area labeled Rocky Mountains.

White and lavender columbine

Colorado blue spruce

Lark bunting

Rocky Mountains: Utah

Write the word **hoodoo** on the blank. Trace over the faint lines and add your own details to illustrate some of the many hoodoos in Utah.

____

an irregular column of weathered rock

1. Look at the state flag, bird, tree, and flower of Utah pictured on this page.
2. Color Utah blue on the map on pages 2-3.
3. Color the star that marks Salt Lake City, the capital of Utah, yellow.
4. Color the Jello-O, the official snack food of Utah, the color of the flavor of your choice.
5. Color the dinosaur fossil at Dinosaur National Monument gray.

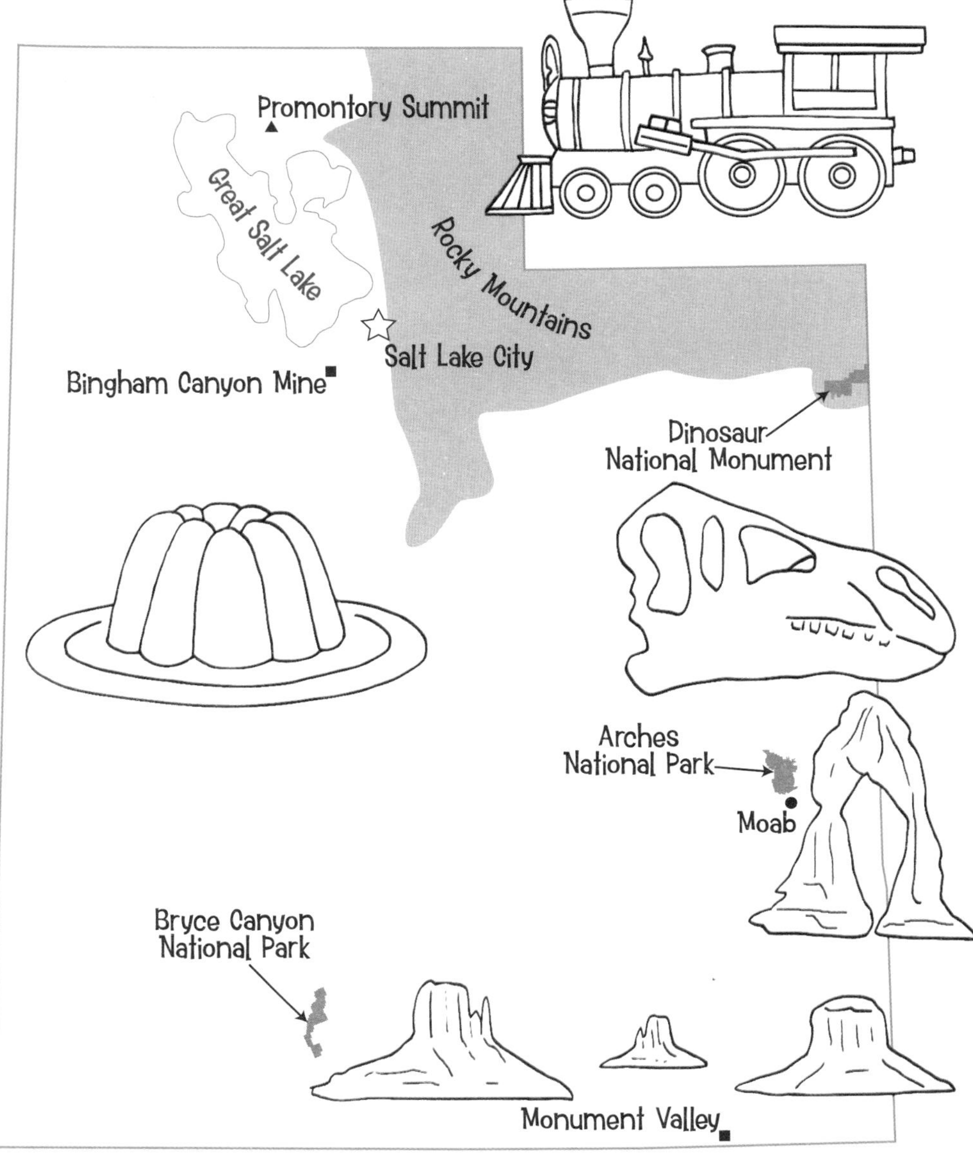

California seagull

6. Color the Great Salt Lake blue.
7. Color the train heading to Promontory Summit red.
8. Draw some hoodoos at Bryce Canyon National Park.
9. Color the monuments in Monument Valley and the arch at Arches National Park reddish-brown.

Quaking aspen

Sego lily

Rocky Mountains: Nevada

Write the word **dam** on the blank. Trace over the faint lines and add your own details to illustrate Hoover Dam in Nevada.

____

a barrier built to hold back water, to make electricity, and to control flooding

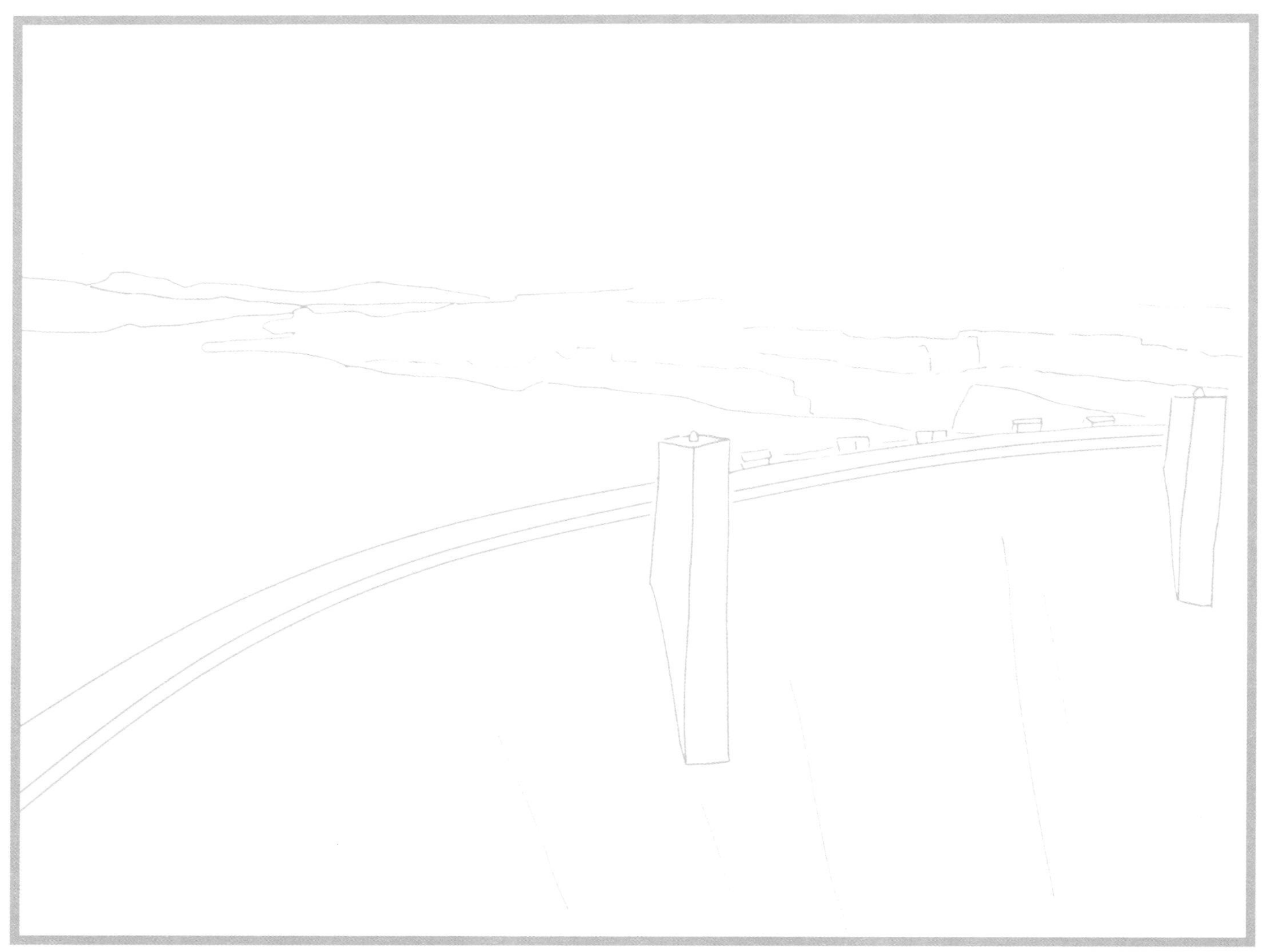

1. Look at the state flag, bird, tree, and flower of Nevada pictured on this page.
2. Color Nevada blue on the map on pages 2-3.
3. Color the star that marks Carson City, the capital of Nevada, yellow.
4. Color the leaves of the bristlecone pine tree green. Color the trunk light brown.
5. Color the American pronghorn racing across the Sheldon National Wildlife Preserve light brown.
6. Color elephant rock in the Valley of Fire reddish-brown.

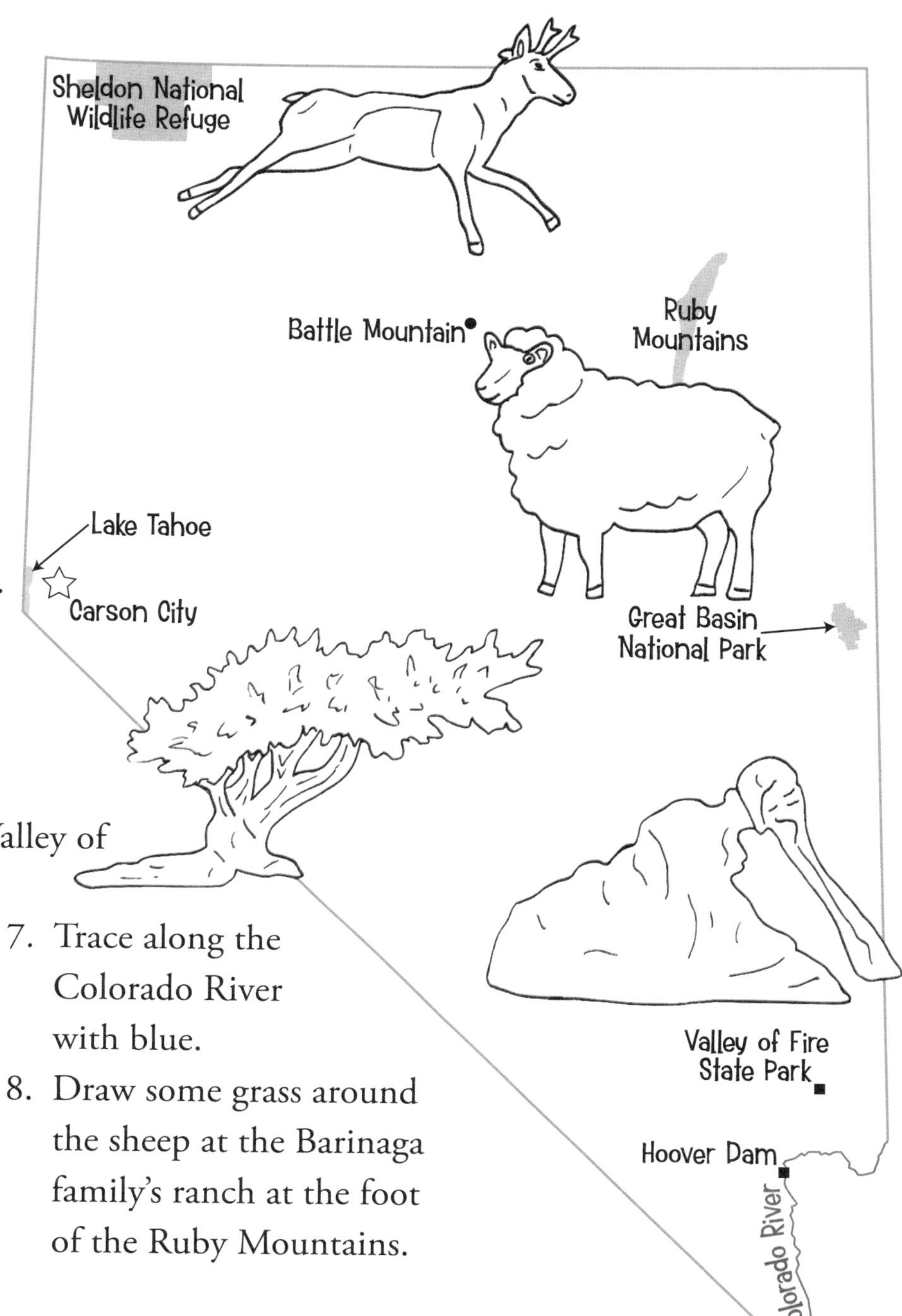

7. Trace along the Colorado River with blue.
8. Draw some grass around the sheep at the Barinaga family's ranch at the foot of the Ruby Mountains.

Single-leaf pinyon

Mountain bluebird

Sagebrush

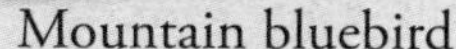

Southwest: Oklahoma

Write the words **salt plains** on the blank. Trace over the faint lines and add your own details to illustrate a boy searching for crystals on the salt plains of Oklahoma.

____

large areas of ground covered with salt and other minerals

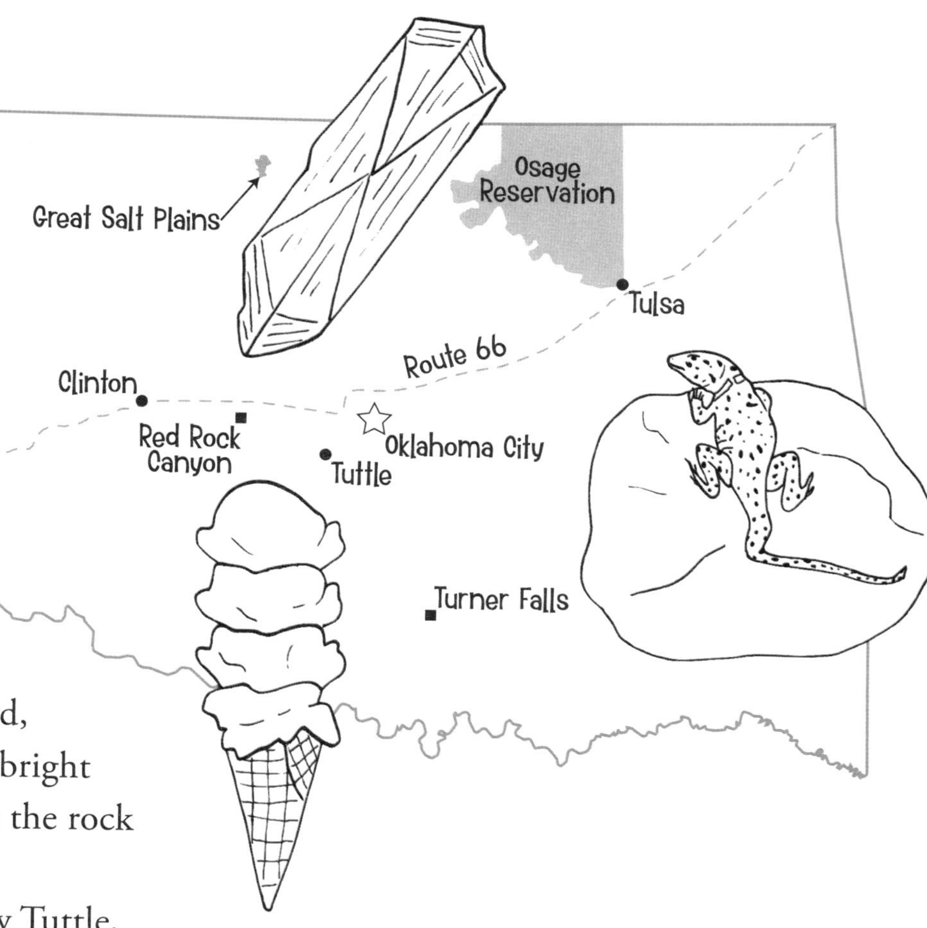

1. Look at the state flag, bird, tree, and flower of Oklahoma pictured on this page.
2. Color Oklahoma yellow on the map on pages 2-3.
3. Color the star that marks Oklahoma City, the capital of Oklahoma, yellow.
4. Color the eastern collared lizard, the state reptile of Oklahoma, bright blue with a yellow head. Color the rock he is scurrying across gray.
5. Color the ice cream cone below Tuttle, and think about the Braum's factory filling 3,000 cartons of ice cream in an hour!
6. Trace along the section of Route 66 that runs through Oklahoma with red.
7. Color the hourglass shape inside the selenite crystal from the Great Salt Plains brown.

Eastern redbud

Oklahoma rose

Scissor-tailed flycatcher

Southwest: Texas

Write the word **ranch** on the blank. Trace over the faint lines and add your own details to illustrate a Texas ranch.

____

a large farm, especially in the western United States and Canada, where people raise livestock

1. Look at the state flag, bird, tree, and flower of Texas pictured on this page.
2. Color Texas yellow on the map on pages 2-3.
3. Color the star that marks Austin, the capital of Texas, yellow.
4. Color the cars sticking out of the ground at Cadillac Ranch near Amarillo with bright, crazy colors.
5. Color the dress of the Mexican dancer performing in El Paso with bright colors.
6. Color the cactus near Big Bend National Park green. Color the flowers at the top of the cactus yellow, red, or pink.
7. Color the Texas cowboy.
8. Draw another old fashioned oil well near Beaumont.

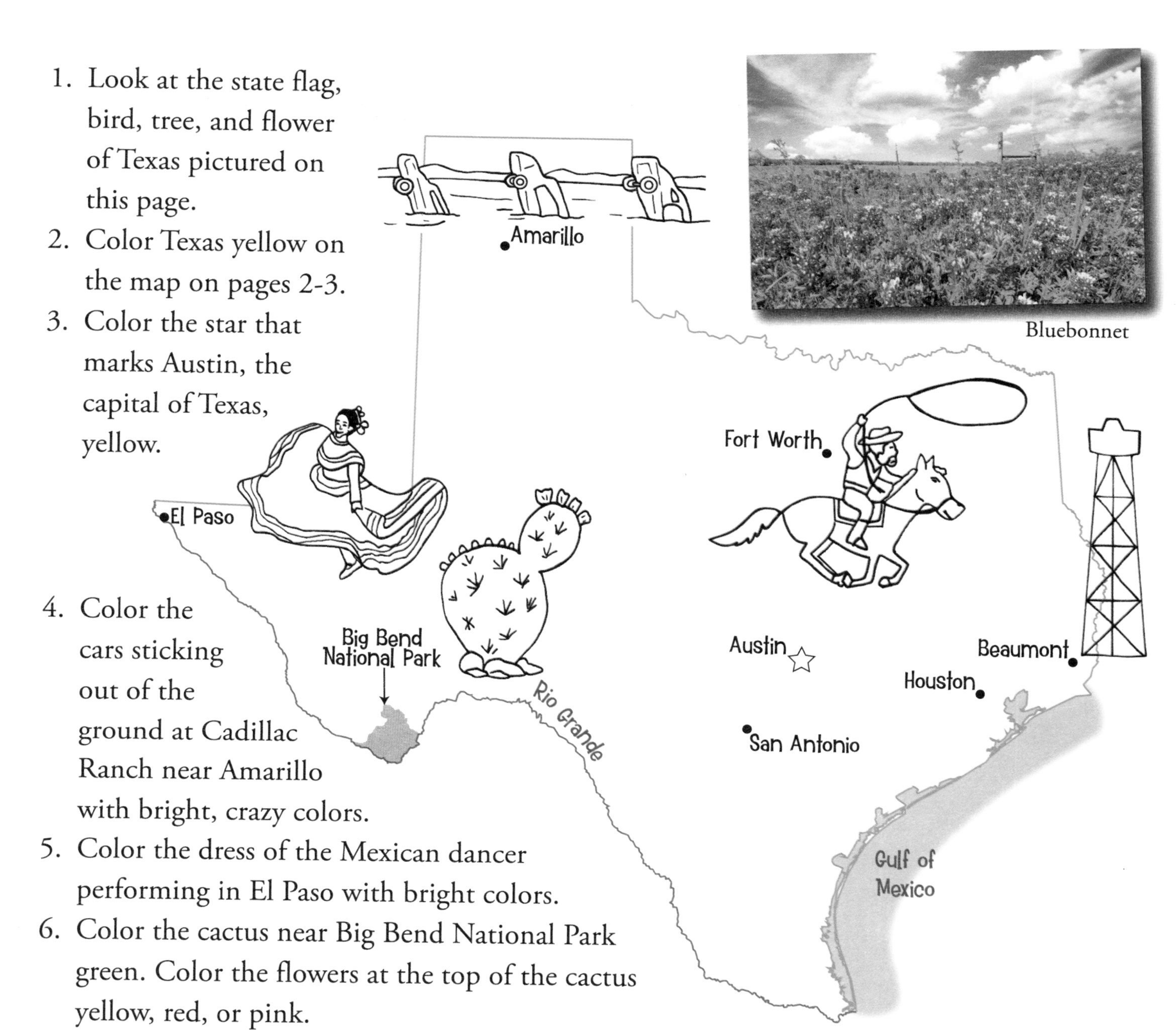

Bluebonnet

Pecan

Mockingbird

Southwest: New Mexico

Write the word **cavate** on the blank. Trace over the faint lines and add your own details to illustrate a cavate in Bandelier National Monument in New Mexico. Make the insides of the cavates very dark.

____

a man-made cave carved into rock

1. Look at the state flag, bird, tree, and flower of New Mexico pictured on this page.
2. Color New Mexico yellow on the map on pages 2-3.
3. Color the star that marks Santa Fe, the capital of New Mexico, yellow.
4. Color the Brazilian free-tailed bat, on his way from Carlsbad Caverns to Mexico for the winter, brown.
5. Color the chile peppers grown in Hatch, the Chile Capital of the World. Color one red and one green, both with green stems.
6. Color the hot air balloon flying over Albuquerque at the International Balloon Fiesta the colors of your choice.
7. Color Shiprock, the Rock with Wings, brown.
8. Write Smokey on the ranger hat in the Lincoln National Forest where the real Smokey Bear was born.

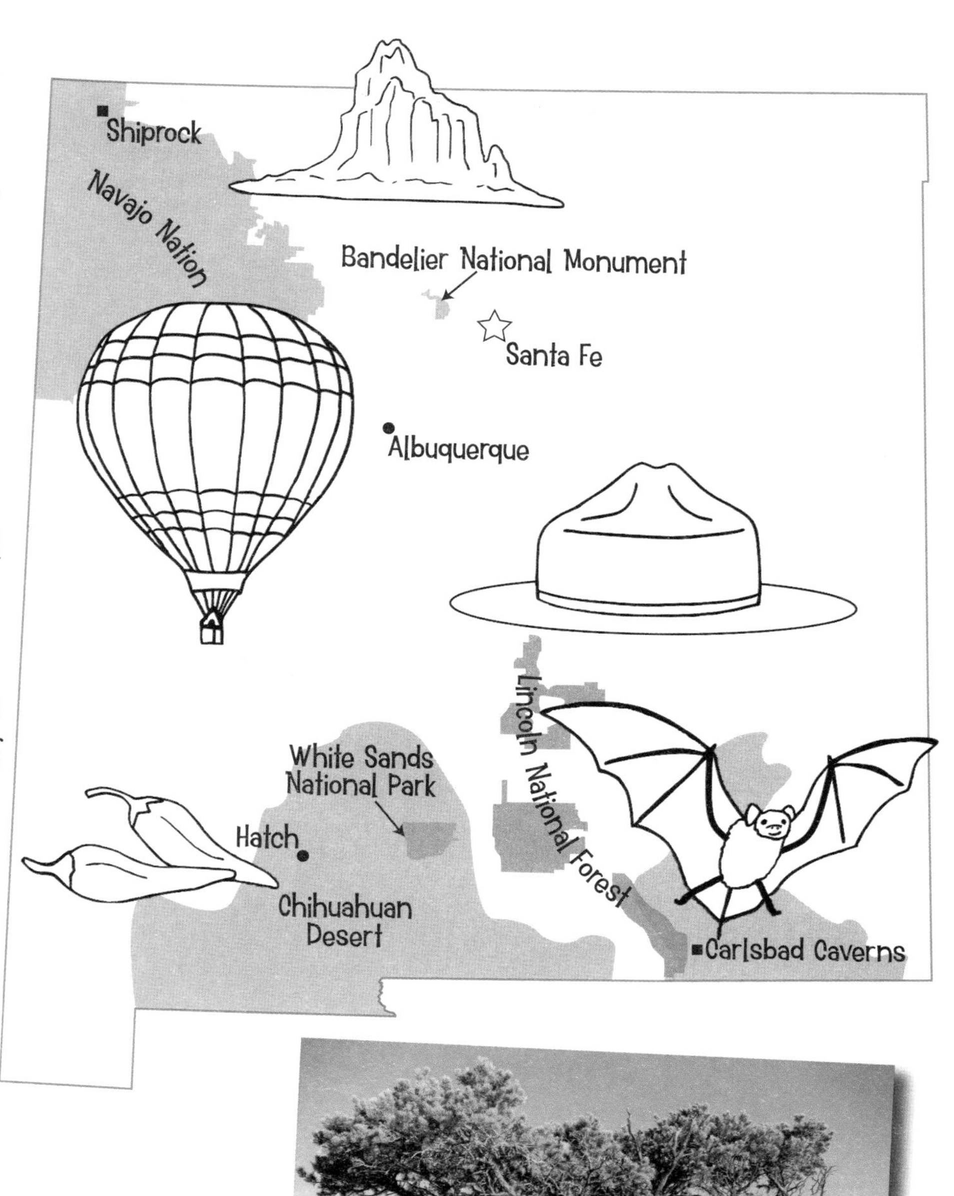

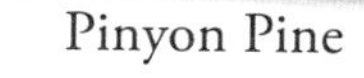
Pinyon Pine

Yucca

Greater roadrunner

Southwest: Arizona

Write the words **dark-sky city** on the blank. Trace over the faint lines and add your own details to the nighttime sky over Flagstaff, Arizona. (Read the instructions below to draw the stars.)

____

a city that has limits on the amount of light allowed to shine at night, which allows the beauty of the stars to be seen better

Before you work on the illustration above, place a piece of cardboard behind this page so you do not make marks on any other pages. To make the stars, find a blunt tool such as a bobby pin or a click pen that is closed—something that you can use to make small indentions on your picture. Practice this technique on scrap paper first! Place a piece of cardboard behind your paper so you do not mark your work surface. Using your blunt tool, press very firmly to make indentions on the scrap paper to make stars in the sky. Color over the indentions with the side of a pencil or colored pencil so that the indentions stay white.

1. Look at the state flag, bird, tree, and flower of Arizona pictured on this page.
2. Color Arizona yellow on the map on pages 2-3.
3. Color the star that marks Phoenix, the capital of Arizona, yellow.
4. Color the gila monster orange.
5. Draw stars over Flagstaff, an International Dark-Sky City.
6. Color the airplane in the aircraft boneyard in Tucson gray.
7. Draw a sun above Yuma, where the sun shines about 90% of the time.
8. Trace along the Colorado River with blue.
9. Color Nampeyo's pottery light brown with a red design.

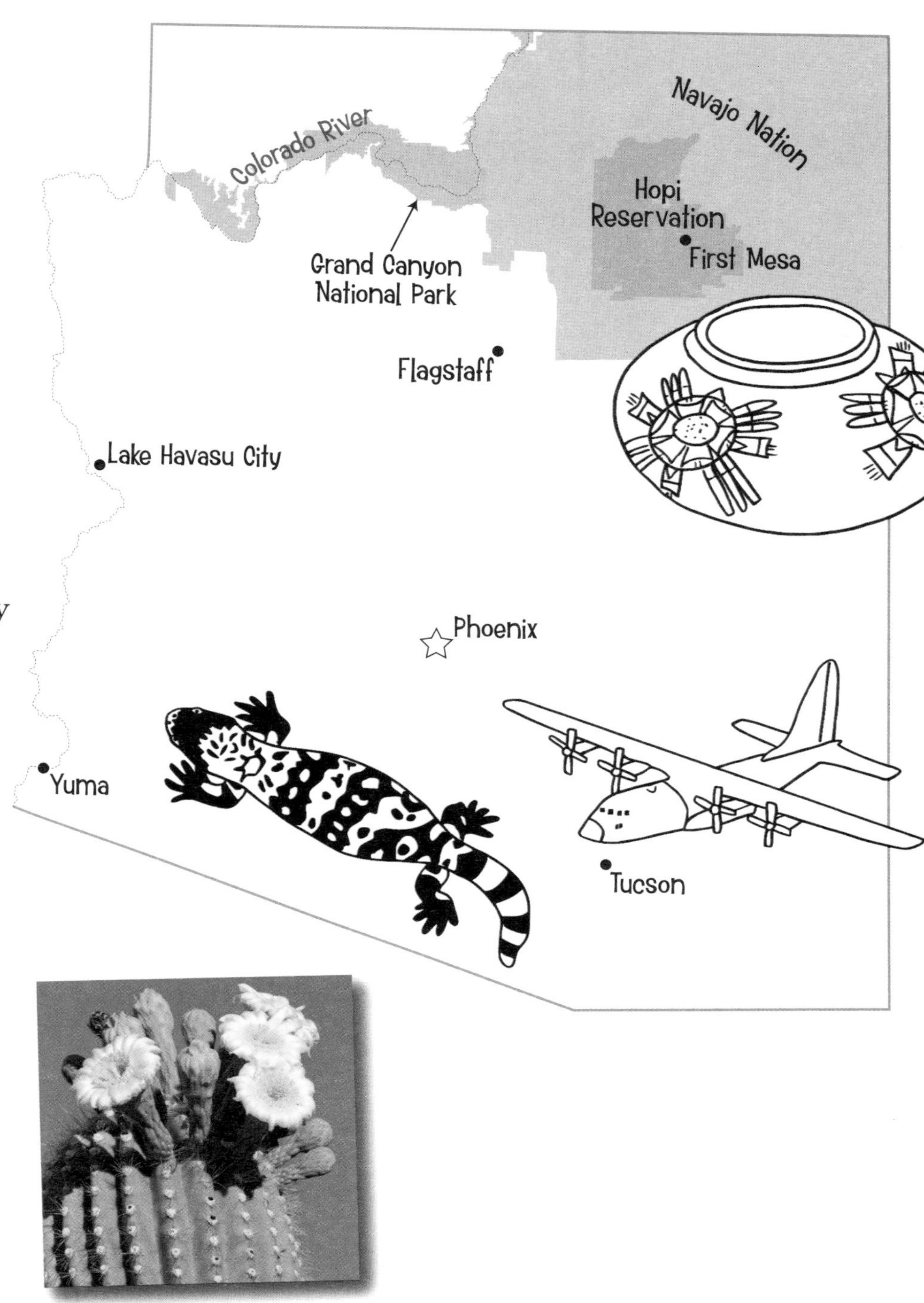

Saguaro cactus blossom

Palo verde

Cactus wren

Pacific: California

Write the word **desert** on the blank. Trace over the faint lines and add your own details to illustrate Death Valley, a desert in California.

____

a barren land
that receives little precipitation

1. Look at the state flag, bird, tree, and flower of California pictured on this page.
2. Color California green on the map on pages 2-3.
3. Color the star that marks Sacramento, the capital of California, yellow.
4. Color the leaves of the General Sherman, the giant sequoia that is the largest tree in the world, green. Color the trunk brown.
5. Color the food that grew in the Central Valley. Color the tomato red, the carrot orange, and the raisins black.
6. Color the silicon chip from the Silicon Valley green.
7. Color the cable car in San Francisco red.

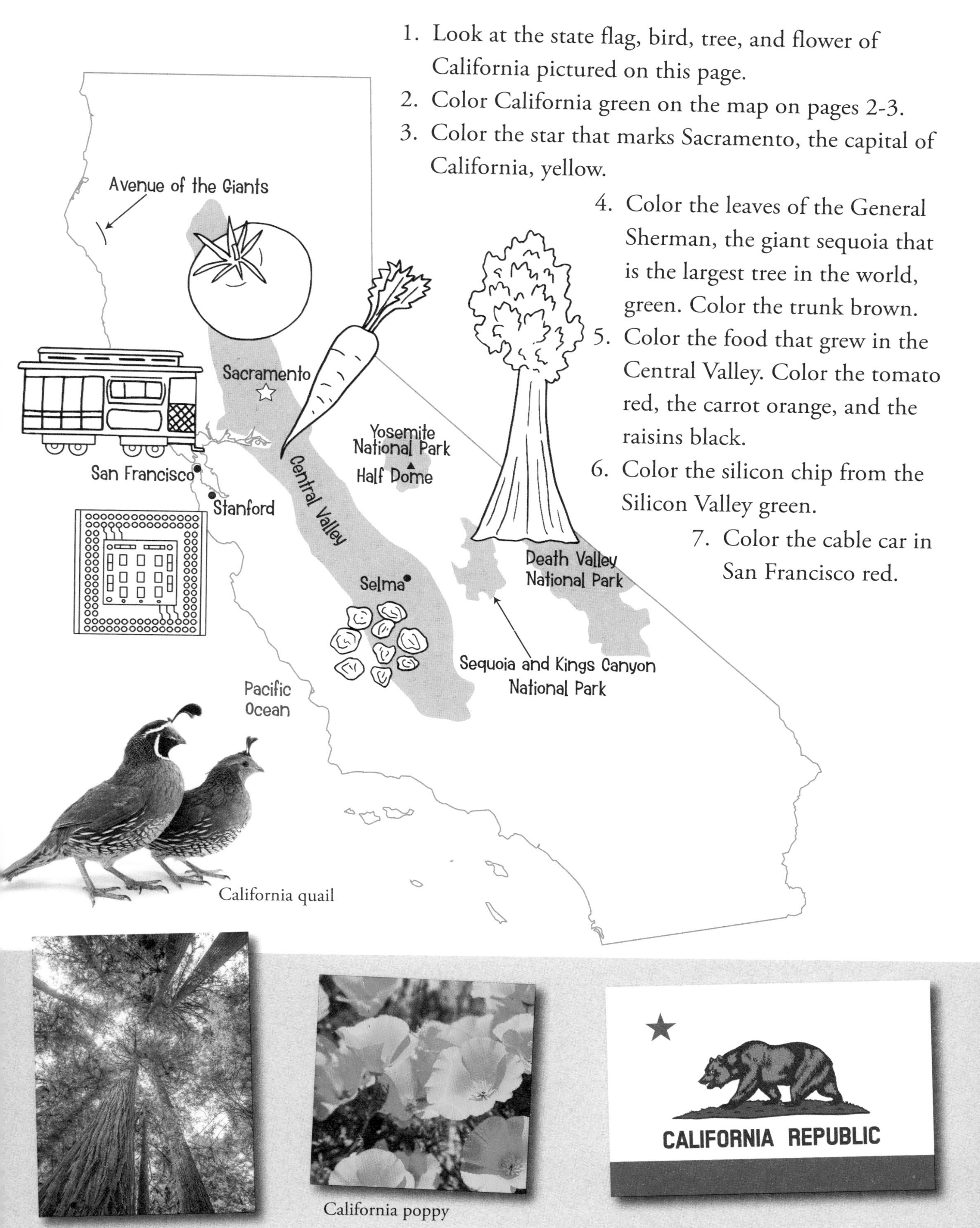

California quail

California redwood

California poppy

Pacific: Oregon

Write the word **caldera** on the blank. Trace over the faint lines and add your own details to illustrate Crater Lake, a caldera in Oregon.

____

a large crater that forms
in a collapsed volcano

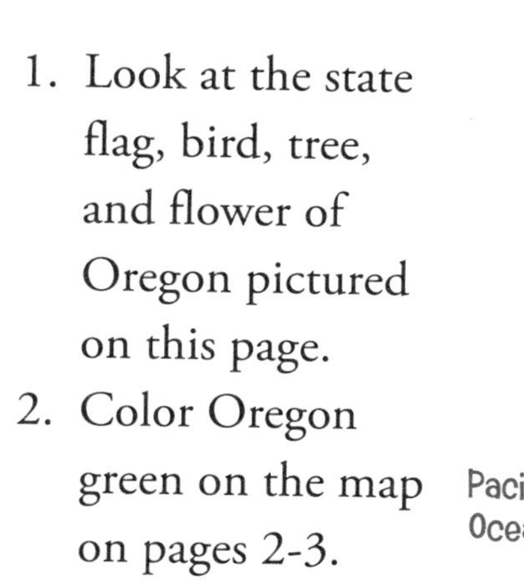

1. Look at the state flag, bird, tree, and flower of Oregon pictured on this page.
2. Color Oregon green on the map on pages 2-3.
3. Color the star that marks Salem, the capital of Oregon, yellow.

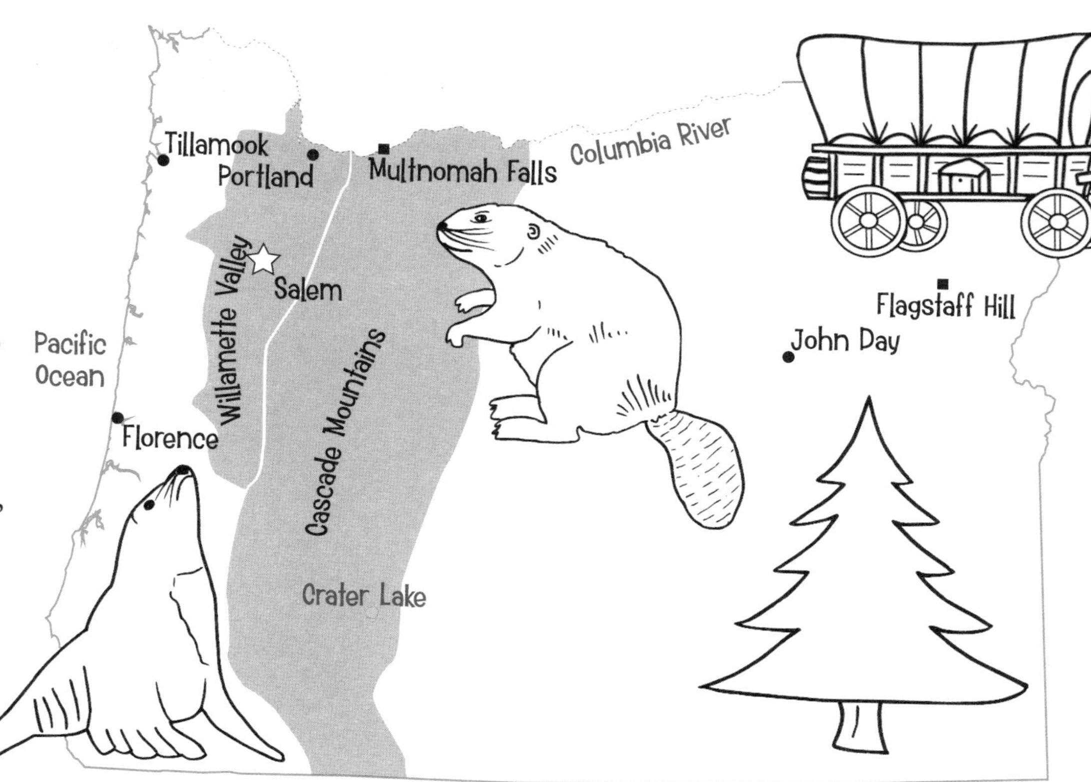

4. Oregon grows more Christmas trees than any other state. Decorate the Christmas tree.
5. Color the beaver, the state animal of Oregon, brown.
6. Color the sea lion at Sea Lion Caves brown.
7. Trace along the Columbia River with blue.
8. Color the wooden parts of the covered wagon that traveled on the Oregon Trail brown (that's everything besides the canvas cover, which you can leave white.).

Oregon grape

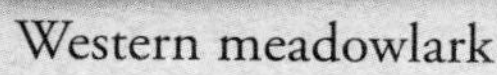
Western meadowlark

Douglas fir

Pacific: Washington

Write the word **sound** on the blank. Trace over the faint lines and add your own details to illustrate Puget Sound in Washington.

____

a large inlet (or arm) of an ocean or sea

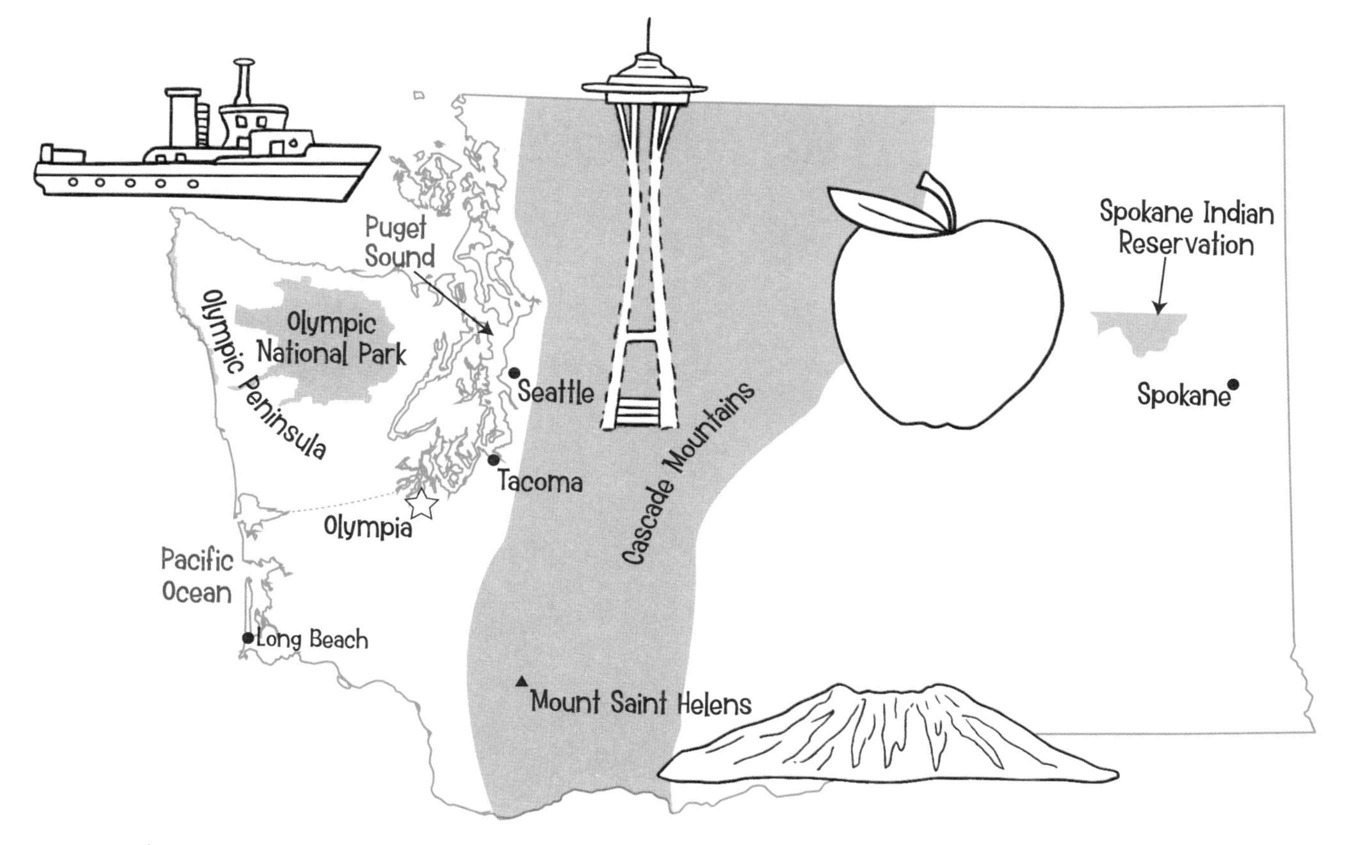

1. Look at the state flag, bird, tree, and flower of Washington pictured on this page.
2. Color Washington green on the map on pages 2-3.
3. Color the star that marks Olympia, the capital of Washington, yellow.
4. Color the apple grown in Washington the color you would like to eat.
5. Use gray to draw smoke coming out of Mount St. Helens to show the eruption of 1980.
6. Draw over the dotted lines on the Space Needle in Seattle.
7. Color the stripe on the Foss tugboat green. Draw waves around it.
8. Color the Olympic Peninsula green (above the dotted line).

Coast rhododendron

Willow goldfinch

Western hemlock

Pacific: Alaska

Write the word **fjord** on the blank. Trace over the faint lines and add your own details to illustrate a fjord in Alaska.

____

a long, narrow inlet of the sea between steep mountains or cliffs

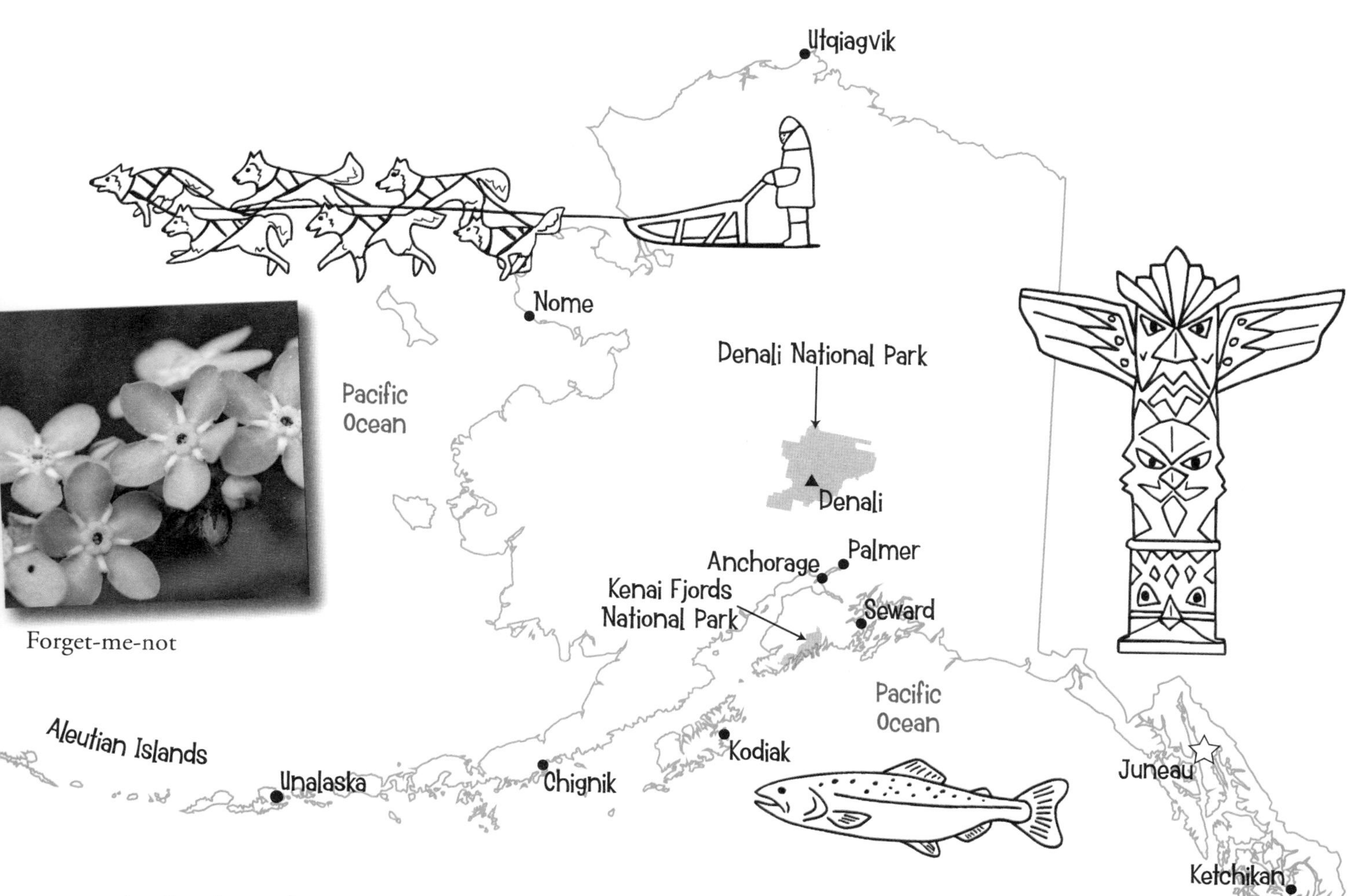

Forget-me-not

1. Look at the state flag, bird, tree, and flower of Alaska pictured on this page.
2. Color Alaska green on the map on pages 108-109.
3. Color the star that marks Juneau, the capital of Alaska, yellow.
4. Make the totem pole colorful.
5. Color the salmon swimming upstream gray.
6. Color the dogsled team and their musher (driver). Use browns, grays, and black to color the dogs.
7. Draw waves around the Aleutian Islands.

Sitka spruce

Willow ptarmigan

Pacific: Hawaii

Write the word **volcano** on the blank. Trace over the faint lines and add your own details to illustrate a volcano in Hawaii.

____

an opening in the earth through which lava, volcanic ash, and gasses escape into the air

Nene

1. Look at the state flag, bird, tree, and flower of Hawaii pictured on this page.
2. Circle Hawaii with a pencil on the map on pages 108-109.
3. Color the star that marks Honolulu, the capital of Hawaii, yellow.
4. Use bright colors to color the flowers on the lei.
5. Color the top of the humpback whale dark gray. Leave it white underneath.
6. Color the spinner dolphin dark gray on top, medium gray in the middle, and light gray underneath.
7. Use red, yellow, and orange to draw lava shooting out of the volcano and running down its sides.
8. Draw waves around the Hawaiian Islands.

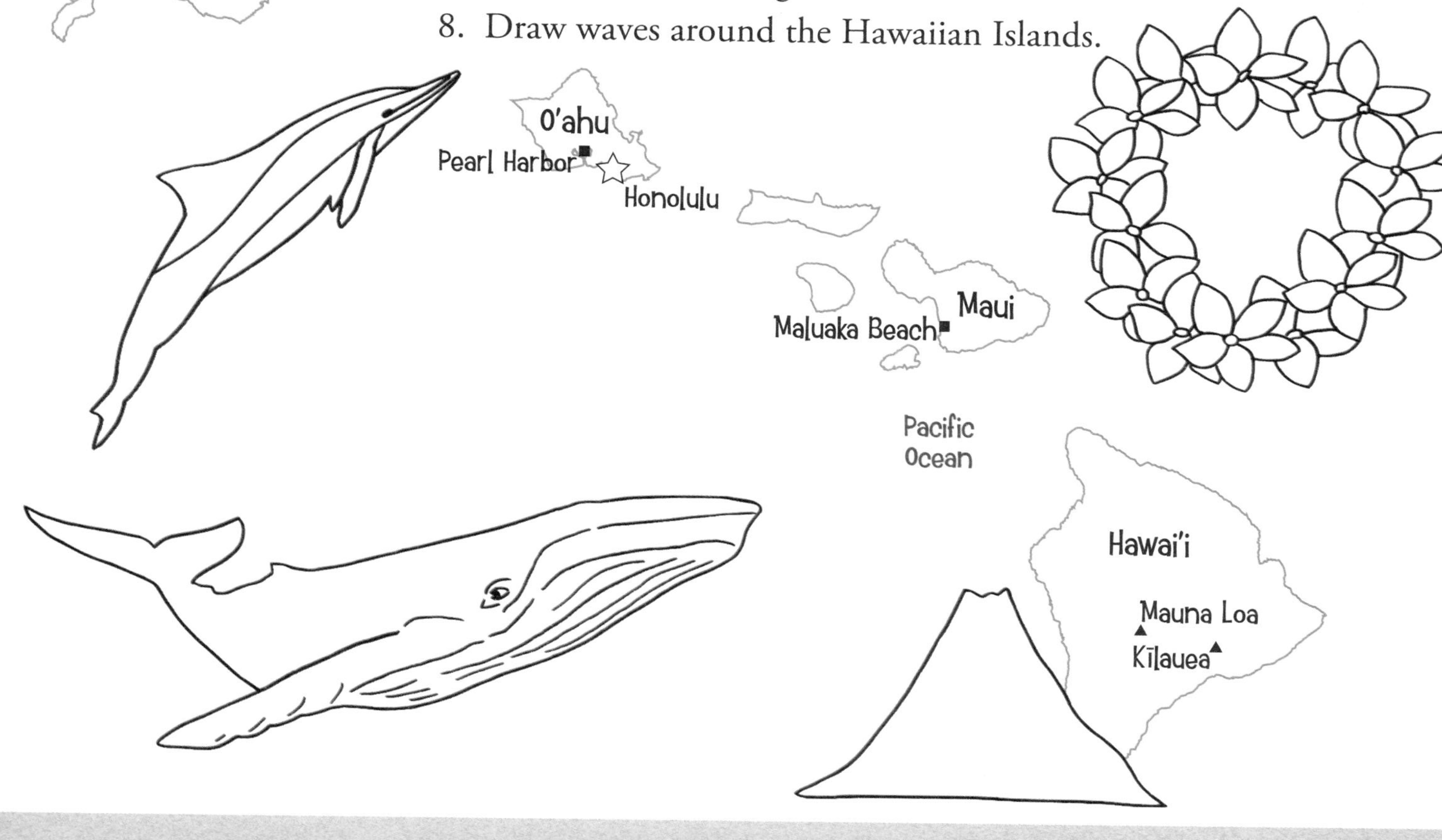

Yellow hibiscus

Kukui

U.S. Territories

Write the word **lagoon** on the blank. Trace over the faint lines and add your own details to illustrate the Secret Lagoon on Tinian, one of the Northern Mariana Islands.

____

a shallow body of salt water that is separated from the sea by a sandbank or coral reef

Yellow trumpetbush (Virgin Islands)

1. Look at the territorial symbols pictured on this page.
2. Circle Puerto Rico, the U.S. Virgin Islands, Guam, the Northern Mariana Islands, and American Samoa with a pencil on the map on pages 108-109.
3. Color the top, middle, and bottom stripes on the flag of Puerto Rico red. Color the triangle blue. Leave the star white.
4. Color the "V" and "I" light blue on the flag of the U.S. Virgin Islands. Color the arrows light blue. Color the branch green.
5. Color the main background of the Guam flag dark blue. Color the outer border and the border around the palm tree red.
6. Color the background of the Northern Mariana Islands flag (including the area inside the wreath) light blue. Color the latte (stone pillar) behind the star gray.
7. Color the two blank areas of the American Samoa flag dark blue. Color the bald eagle brown (leaving his head and tail white).

Puerto Rican woodpecker
(Puerto Rico)

Mariana fruit dove
(Northern Mariana Islands)

Paogo
(American Samoa)

gainvillea
(Guam)

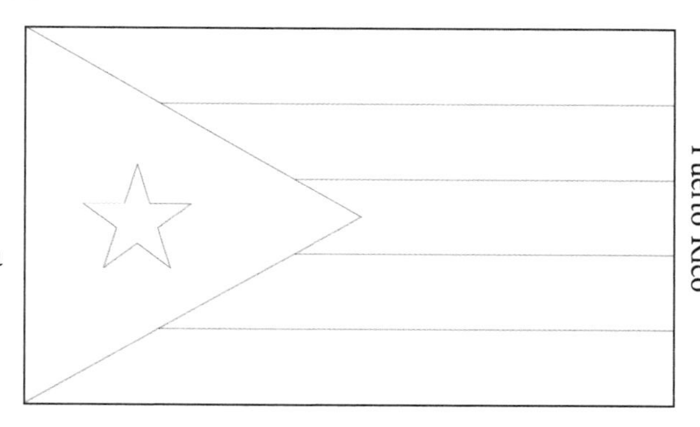

Puerto Rico

U.S. Virgin Islands

Guam

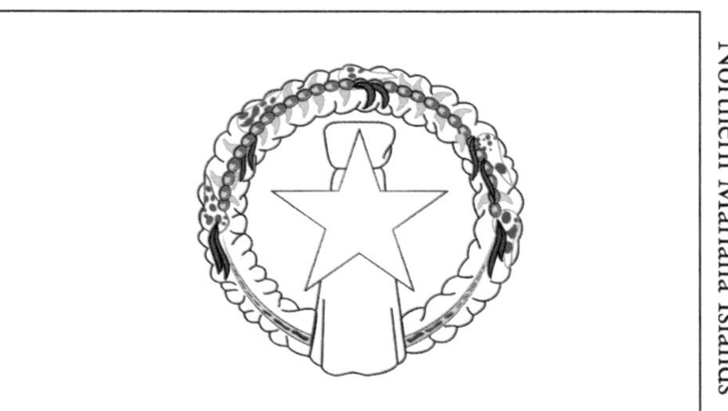

Northern Mariana Islands

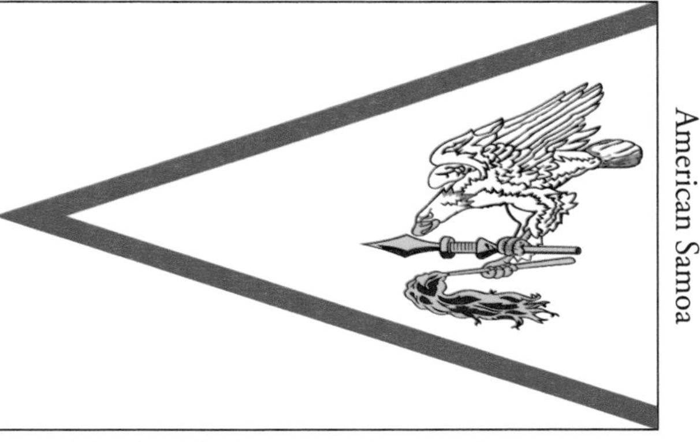

American Samoa

Pacific Ocean

Hawaii

Northern Mariana Islands

Guam

Equator

American Samoa

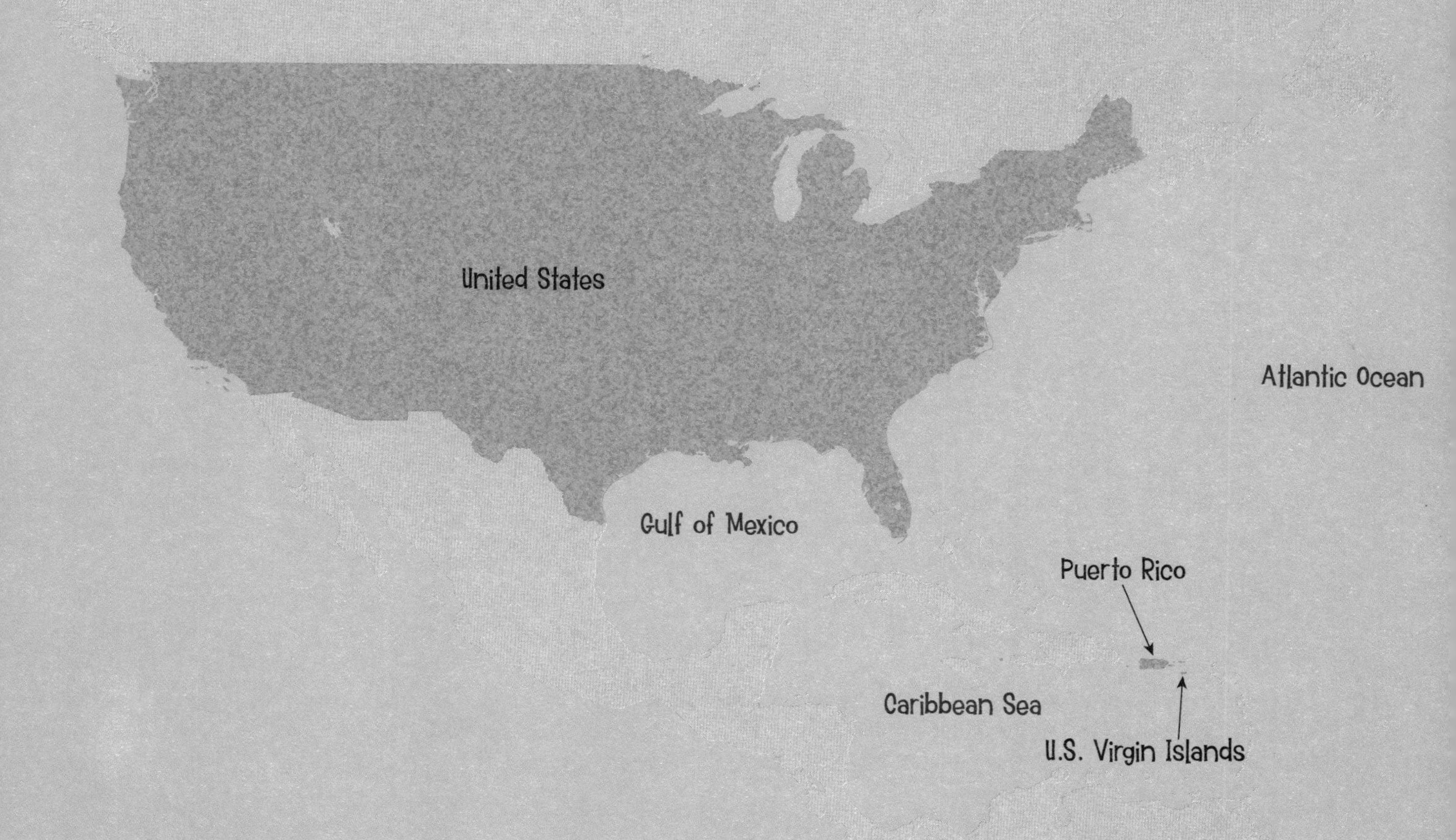
United States
Atlantic Ocean
Gulf of Mexico
Puerto Rico
Caribbean Sea
U.S. Virgin Islands
Equator
Pacific Ocean

Image Credits

Maps - Nate McCurdy
(Outlines by Vladimir Sviracevic / Shutterstock.com)

Hand-drawn illustrations - Anna Higgins

State flags - grebeshkovmaxim / Shutterstock.com
(except where noted)

Images marked with one of these codes are used with the permission of a Creative Commons Attribution or Attribution-Share Alike License. See the websites listed for details.
CC BY 2.0 creativecommons.org/licenses/by/2.0/
CC BY-SA 2.0 creativecommons.org/licenses/by-sa/2.0/
CC BY-SA 3.0 creativecommons.org/licenses/by-sa/3.0/

4 Darryl Brooks / Shutterstock.com
5 Chickadee - Charles Brutlag / Shutterstock.com; Pine - Ukrolenochka / Shutterstock.com
6 sebastienlemyre / Shutterstock.com
7 Lilac - vilax / Shutterstock.com; Birch - John A. Anderson / Shutterstock.com; Finch - Robert L Kothenbeutel / Shutterstock.com
8 ChristineMinato / Shutterstock.com
9 Maple - Le Do / Shutterstock.com; Thrush - Paul Reeves Photography / Shutterstock.com; Clover - Viesturs Ozolins / Shutterstock.com
10 Scott Varisco / Shutterstock.com
11 Chickadee - Steve Byland / Shutterstock.com; Mayflower - Jeff Holcombe / Shutterstock.com; Elm - Jay Yuan / Shutterstock.com
12 JonPeckham / Shutterstock.com
13 Maple - ClubhouseArts / Shutterstock.com; Violet - Kimberly Boyles / Shutterstock.com
14 Elizabeth C Waters / Shutterstock.com
15 Robin - David Spates / Shutterstock.com; Mountain laurel - Jeff Holcombe / Shutterstock.com; Charter Oak - Wadsworth Atheneum, Hartford, Connecticut
16 Ruben Martinez Barricarte / Shutterstock.com
17 Bluebird - Steve Byland / Shutterstock.com; Maple - Nancy Kennedy / Shutterstock.com; Rose - Detailfoto / Shutterstock.com
18 Jay Mudaliar / Shutterstock.com
19 Mountain laurel - jadimages / Shutterstock.com; Eastern hemlock - Andrew Williams / Shutterstock.com; Ruffled grouse - Mircea Costina / Shutterstock.com
20 Khairil Azhar Junos / Shutterstock.com
21 Violet - Volosina / Shutterstock.com; Red oaks - anmbph / Shutterstock.com; Goldfinch - Andrew David Miller / Shutterstock.com
22 Gerald Marella / Shutterstock.com
23 Hen - lunamarina / Shutterstock.com; Holly - CristiDumi / Shutterstock.com; Peach blossom - Vasilius / Shutterstock.com
24 Andrew F. Kazmierski / Shutterstock.com
25 Oriole - Mike Truchon / Shutterstock.com; White oak - Quarterczar / Wikimedia Commons; Black-eyed susan - Kristy Lester / Shutterstock.com
26 MGS / Shutterstock.com
27 Scarlet oak - Photonaturepaysage / Shutterstock.com; Wood thrush - Paul Reeves Photography / Shutterstock.com; Flag - Svetocheck / Shutterstock.com
28 Joe Ravi / Shutterstock.com
29 Dogwood flower - Melinda Fawver / Shutterstock.com; Tree - Noel V. Baebler / Shutterstock.com; Cardinal - Sari ONeal / Shutterstock.com
30 Yoshiyuki Takahashi / Shutterstock.com
31 Cardinal - Dean Fikar / Shutterstock.com; Maple - Malachi Jacobs / Shutterstock.com; Rhododrendron - nissia / Shutterstock.com
32 Jim Vallee / Shutterstock.com
33 Goldenrod - Scisetti Alfio / Shutterstock.com; Tulip poplar - Nikolay Kurzenko / Shutterstock.com; Cardinals - Bonnie Taylor Barry / Shutterstock.com
34 gracious_tiger / Shutterstock.com

35 Tulip poplar - Yanosh Nemesh / Shutterstock.com; Mockingbird - Bonnie Taylor Barry / Shutterstock.com; Iris - Ruth Swan / Shutterstock.com
36 Ryan McGurl / Shutterstock.com
37 Cardinal - Steve Byland / Shutterstock.com; Dogwood - Jorge Salcedo / Shutterstock.com; Pine - digidreamgrafix / Shutterstock.com
38 National Park Service
39 Wren - IrinaK / Shutterstock.com; Palmetto - Cathy Brinkworth / Shutterstock.com; Yellow jessamine - WenCap / Shutterstock.com
40 Deborah Ferrin / Shutterstock.com
41 Brown thrasher - Brian A Wolf / Shutterstock.com; Cherokee rose - tamu1500 / Shutterstock.com; Live oak - Gary C. Tognoni / Shutterstock.com
42 Alabama Pioneers
43 Camellia - Videowokart / Shutterstock.com; Pine - Nikolay Kurzenko / Shutterstock.com; Northern flicker - karamysh / Shutterstock.com
44 EyeTravel / Shutterstock.com
45 Tree - Denton Rumsey / Shutterstock.com; Mockingbird - Skyler Ewing / Shutterstock.com
46 Bram Reusen / Shutterstock.com
47 Apple blossom - oksana2010 / Shutterstock.com; Trees - Sadie Lou Hays / Shutterstock.com; Mockingbird - Tim Zurowski / Shutterstock.com
48 Jayne Chapman / Shutterstock.com
49 Bald cypress - Steve Bower / Shutterstock.com; Pelican - BMJ / Shutterstock.com; Magnolia - MILA PARH / Shutterstock.com
50 National Archives and Records Administration
51 Sabal palm - Thomas Barrat / Shutterstock.com; Mockingbird - Jill Nightingale / Shutterstock.com; Orange blossom - 1JMueller / Shutterstock.com
52 Steven Schremp / Shutterstock.com
53 Apple blossoms - LiliGraphie / Shutterstock.com; Pine - Pam Carnell / Shutterstock.com; Robin - Tony Savino / Shutterstock.com
54 Hunter Kauffman / Shutterstock.com
55 Cardinal - Elliotte Rusty Harold / Shutterstock.com; Buckeye - CountryGirl624 / Shutterstock.com; Carnation - Mikhail Romanov / Shutterstock.com
56 Jay_Sturner / Wikimedia Commons / CC BY 2.0
57 Peony - Mikhail Abramov / Shutterstock.com; Cardinal - Richard G Smith / Shutterstock.com; Tulip poplar - Nikolay Kurzenko / Shutterstock.com
58 Jason Patrick Ross / Shutterstock.com
59 Acorns - Luis Carlos Jimenez del rio / Shutterstock.com; Cardinal - Connie Barr / Shutterstock.com; Violet - Vadim ZH / Shutterstock.com
60 Ti / Shutterstock.com
61 Violet - Volosina / Shutterstock.com; Maple - Brandon Blinkenberg / Shutterstock.com; Robin - gregg williams / Shutterstock.com
62 KDLM Radio
63 Lady's slipper - Holly Kuchera / Shutterstock.com; Loon - Agnieszka Bacal / Shutterstock.com; Red pine - Naeema Mamode Ally / Shutterstock.com
64 MikeHardyPhotography / Shutterstock.com
65 Goldfinch - Mike Truchon / Shutterstock.com; Oak - Aleksandr Stepanchuk / Shutterstock.com; Wild rose - Ruth Swan / Shutterstock.com
66 Fredlyfish4 / Shutterstock.com
67 Bluebird - Steve Byland / Shutterstock.com; Hawthorn - Alexander Shodai / Shutterstock.com; Dogwood - rck_953 / Shutterstock.com
68 Robert D Brozek / Shutterstock.com
69 Meadowlark - Michael Chatt / Shutterstock.com; Cottonwood - Ann Cantelow / Shutterstock.com; Sunflower - Sari ONeal / Shutterstock.com
70 Microgen / Shutterstock.com
71 Meadowlark - Michael Chatt / Shutterstock.com; Cottonwood - Ann Cantelow / Shutterstock.com; Goldenrod - Gl0ck / Shutterstock.com
72 Joseph Sohm / Shutterstock.com
73 Pheasant - Adam Fichna / Shutterstock.com; Spruce - South Dakota State Government; American pasque - Gchapel / Shutterstock.com
74 Andrew Tuttle / Shutterstock.com
75 Meadowlark - Jennifer Bosvert / Shutterstock.com; Wild prairie rose - Photoglitz / Shutterstock.com; Elm - Tim Evanson / Flickr / CC BY-SA 2.0
76 National Park Service
77 Pine - Andrew Orlemann / Shutterstock.com; Bitterroot - KaeCsImages / Shutterstock.com; Meadowlark - vagabond54 / Shutterstock.com
78 Gregory Johnston / Shutterstock.com
79 Bluebird - CAspinwall / Shutterstock.com; syringa - Nikki Yancey / Shutterstock.com; Pine - Robert Mutch / Shutterstock.com
80 Zack Frank / Shutterstock.com
81 Meadowlark - Sarah Jessup / Shutterstock.com; Cottonwood - rCarner / Shutterstock.com; Indian paintbrush - Jody Ann / Shutterstock.com
82 Anton Foltin / Shutterstock.com
83 Columbine - wallybird / Shutterstock.com; Spruce - Leonid S. Shtandel / Shutterstock.com; Lark bunting - Cindy Creighton / Shutterstock.com

84 Johnny Adolphson / Shutterstock.com
85 Segull - Spectruminfo / Shutterstock.com; Aspen - Don Mammoser / Shutterstock.com; Sego lily - MichaelSy / Shutterstock.com
86 Matej Hudovernik / Shutterstock.com
87 Pinyon - Joseph Foley / Shutterstock.com; Bluebird - David Spates / Shutterstock.com; Sagebrush - Joseph Foley / Shutterstock.com
88 IrinaK / Shutterstock.com
89 Redbud - Mark Allen Robinson / Shutterstock.com; Oklahoma rose - NMTD MEDIA / Shutterstock.com; Scissor-tailed flycatcher - Natalia Kuzmina / Shutterstock.com
90 Quinn Calder / Shutterstock.com
91 Bluebonnet - Dean Fikar / Shutterstock.com; Pecan - tayloradempsey / Shutterstock.com; Mockingbird - tayloradempsey / Shutterstock.com
92 Traveller70 / Shutterstock.com
93 Pinyon pine - Andrew Orlemann / Shutterstock.com; Yucca - Katrina Leigh / Shutterstock.com; Roadrunner - Frank Fichtmueller / Shutterstock.com
94 Will Alpert / Shutterstock.com
95 Saguaro cactus blossoms - Bill Florence / Shutterstock.com; Palo verde - Paul R. Jones / Shutterstock.com; Cactus wren - Julie A. Curtis / Shutterstock.com
96 Scott Prokop / Shutterstock.com
97 Quail - photomaster / Shutterstock.com; Redwoods - Naomi Derby / Shutterstock.com; California poppy - dualpics / Shutterstock.com
98 lu_sea / Shutterstock.com
99 Oregon grape - melei5 / Shutterstock.com; Meadowlark - David Spates / Shutterstock.com; Douglas fir - Hugh K Telleria / Shutterstock.com
100 Chris Ballance / Flickr / CC BY 2.0
101 Rhododendron - Ollga P / Shutterstock.com; Goldfinch - Charles Bergman / Shutterstock.com; Hemlock - Alex O'Neal / Flickr / CC BY-SA 2.0
102 MH Anderson Photography / Shutterstock.com
103 Forget-me-not - cherryyblossom / Shutterstock.com; Ptarmigan - V. Belov / Shutterstock.com; Spruce - Aaron CC BY 2.0; Flag - Dmitriy NDM / Shutterstock.com
104 Fredy Thuerig / Shutterstock.com
105 Nene - Jane McIlroy / Shutterstock.com; Hibiscus - aimful / Shutterstock.com; Kukui - Theodore Trimmer / Shutterstock.com
106 RaksyBH / Shutterstock.com
107 Yellow trumpetbush - MT.PHOTOSTOCK / Shutterstock.com; Woodpecker - John weast / Shutterstock.com; Dove - DickDaniels / Wikimedia Commons / CC BY-SA 3.0; Paogo - Evgeny Drablenkov / Shutterstock.com; Bougainvillea - Scisetti Alfio / Shutterstock.com; Puerto Rico - infinetsoft / Shutterstock.com; U.S. Virgin Islands - Svetocheck / Shutterstock.com; Guam - Vladimir Sviracevic / Shutterstock.com; Northern Mariana Islands - Loveshop / Shutterstock.com; American Samoa - Abdulloh Jehyapar / Shutterstock.com

Our 50 States Atlas Workbook

ISBN 978-1-60999-150-0

Cover and interior design by Mary Evelyn Notgrass McCurdy
Cover images by Patricia Elaine Thomas (boats in Maine) and Ryan Goog Varin (balloon) / Shutterstock.com

Printed in the United States of America

NOTGRASS HISTORY

975 Roaring River Road
Gainesboro, TN 38562
1-800-211-8793 • www.notgrass.com